ROLLING ON

TWO HUNDRED YEARS OF

IRON AND
STEEL

ROLLING ON

TWO HUNDRED YEARS OF

IRON AND
STEEL

CARLEE TRESSEL ALSON

First Edition 2020
Hardcover ISBN: 978-1-950843-40-4
Paperback ISBN: 978-1-950843-39-8

Parafine Press
5322 Fleet Avenue, Cleveland, Ohio 44105
www.parafinepress.com
Cover and book design by Meredith Pangrace
Cover image adapted from *Steel Industry* by Howard Norton Cook, 1936, buon fresco,
126 x 209 in (320 x 530.9 cm); Commissioned through the Section of Fine Arts,1934 - 1943,
Fine Arts Collection, U.S. General Services Administration

For the men and women of Blair Strip Steel,
BelleFlex Technologies,
PulFlex Technologies,
Elliott-Blair Cold Roll Steel,
Shoenberger, Blair, & Co.,
Blair Iron and Steel,
American Steeled Rail,
McKelvey & Blair Cast-Steel and File,
and
for the Blair family, who made it all possible.

TABLE OF CONTENTS

FOREWORD

I n the 1970s, I attended Charles F. Brush High School, which was named for a great inventor forgotten by history. In 1878, Brush invented an arc lighting system that would bring street lighting to Cleveland for the first time in history, then to Detroit, New York, London, and the world. That may have been significant for a while, but not long enough to compete with Thomas Edison for a spot in history.

Interestingly, Mr. Brush may be coming back around. He also invented the first wind-driven electric turbine in 1887. Located in his backyard, the turbine generated electricity for Brush's home for twenty years uninterrupted. Now that modern wind turbines based on Brush's technology are sprouting up on land and sea to provide clean, renewable energy around the world, Mr. Brush's work might make it into what we acknowledge as history worth carrying forward.

Philosopher George Santayana said:

> History, by its nature, must limit the number of famous names
> and events it chronicles—lest it take a lifetime to study a
> lifetime. In actuality, though, for every known historical figure,
> there are thousands, perhaps millions, more men and women of
> equal or greater accomplishment whose names fall outside the
> limit required to educate the future of the applicable past.

Written history has an even harder time recalling groups or families that made significant contributions unless they were powerful ruling families and dynasties. While we have the Curies of science, the Rothschilds of finance, and the Medicis of politics, there is little else that history carries forward about families that made a difference over many generations. Sadly so, because the US Small Business Administration states that companies with fewer than 500 workers account for 99.7 percent of businesses, companies with fewer than 20 workers make up 89.6 percent of businesses, and about half of the gross domestic product of the United States is generated by small businesses.

Even so, small businesses and entrepreneurs gain a microscopic percentage of today's business news and have little shot at history. While this is the reality of being small, educators, students, and anyone looking for organizational strategies can find effective guidance if they take a closer look at some of America's oldest businesses run by families.

One such family is the Blairs of Western Pennsylvania. Now in their tenth generation since arriving in Britain's American colonies more than 250 years ago, the Blairs are still successfully operating a small family business today. I have been fortunate beyond words to work with the Blair family for a mere twenty of those years, more as curator and custodian than president. The current company is Blair Strip Steel in New Castle, Pennsylvania, now ninety-seven years old. It was preceded by many more entities along the way, as the Blair family continually reinvented itself to match the demands of the iron and steel markets of their time.

Given the Blairs' long history of excellent leadership, there was healthy skepticism amongst the board of directors when I came to Blair as the first non-family member to operate the company. However, not long into a discussion of business philosophy, I happened to refer to E.F. Schumacher's book, *Small is Beautiful: Economics as If People Mattered*, which I had read while attending Mr. Brush's high school. Dike Blair, then almost ninety years old and with fifty-five years on the board, immediately and accurately recited Schumacher's advice that, "Any intelligent fool can make things bigger and more complex . . . It takes a touch of genius—and a lot of courage—to move in the opposite direction." At that time and still today Blair is a small company; or, more precisely, it is "right-sized" for the specialty market it serves.

My careful response to Dike Blair and the directors was a paraphrase of Schumacher's point, which underlies this book: "What is the meaning of democracy, freedom, human dignity, standard of living, self-realization, fulfillment? Is it a matter of goods, or of people? Of course it is a matter of people. But people can be themselves only in small comprehensible groups." It was as if I had guessed the secret code words to Blair: business as if people mattered.

In several well-chosen words lies the magic of the Blair family, of their small businesses, and millions of other successful small business enterprises throughout time and across the globe. That is, if business depends on people and people are more likely to operate to their fullest potential in small groups, then it must also be true that small business operates more efficiently, more effectively, and gets the best out of the skill, knowledge, and dreams of its people.

In this book, author Carlee Tressel Alson follows the trail of the Blairs from their arrival in the American colonies in the 1700s to Western

Pennsylvania today. The Blairs were not unique, of course, in coming from Scotland to Pennsylvania, nor evolving from ironmakers to steelmakers, nor proving that hard work brings reward at many levels. But they are nearly unique in persevering, so far, for eight amazing generations.

The Family Business Institute says that only 30 percent of family businesses successfully pass along their business to a second generation, then only 12 percent to a third generation, and 5 percent to a fourth generation. The odds after that fade quickly into very small numbers. So rarely does a family make it eight generations that we must admit from the start that good health and good luck are a meaningful part of the recipe for longevity. Beyond that, however, the recipe starts focusing on good character and good agility for avoiding disaster.

In so many modern contexts, the word "sustainability" is used as the goal of resource and business management. Yet, the best roadmaps for sustainability are not always in front of us but often behind us, in the historical record of companies that have spanned generations. It reminds me of a trip my wife, Peeps, and I took to Greenland, where the Inuits have sustained themselves on the icy edge of a frozen island for more than 17,000 years. How can mankind not celebrate these amazing people and study them as a template for the laws, the family structures, nutrition, community practices, education, and lifestyles that promote sustainability? How have they sustained themselves in such harsh conditions for so many thousands of years? The short answer is they have kept their lives simple and small.

Along the path of *Rolling On: Two Hundred Years of Blair Iron and Steel*, Alson lets you discover those bits of the template yourself but ensures that you understand the ingredients of the recipe in the end.

Finally, Santayana also said, reflecting on the lives of those that history forgot: "They may not have known the foundational success of their life— but we know it now and can relive, retell, reflect, and honor that success."

Let us learn, apply, and pass that foundation along.

Bruce Kinney
Chairman and CEO of Blair Strip Steel

New Castle, Pennsylvania
February 2020

THE BLAIRS OF THE BLAIR STRIP STEEL COMPANY

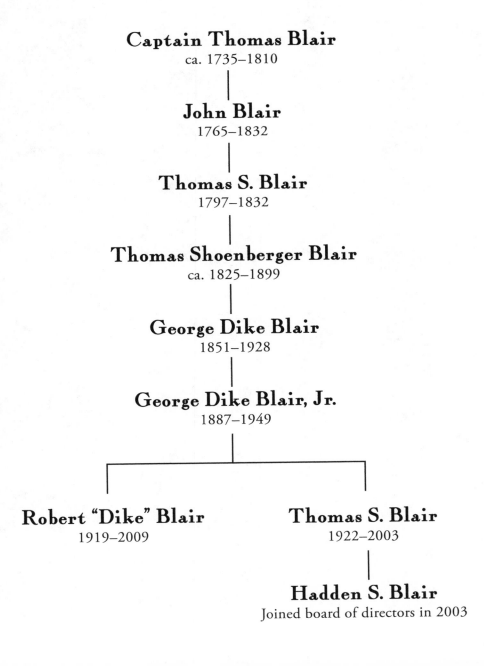

Captain Thomas Blair
ca. 1735–1810

John Blair
1765–1832

Thomas S. Blair
1797–1832

Thomas Shoenberger Blair
ca. 1825–1899

George Dike Blair
1851–1928

George Dike Blair, Jr.
1887–1949

Robert "Dike" Blair
1919–2009

Thomas S. Blair
1922–2003

Hadden S. Blair
Joined board of directors in 2003

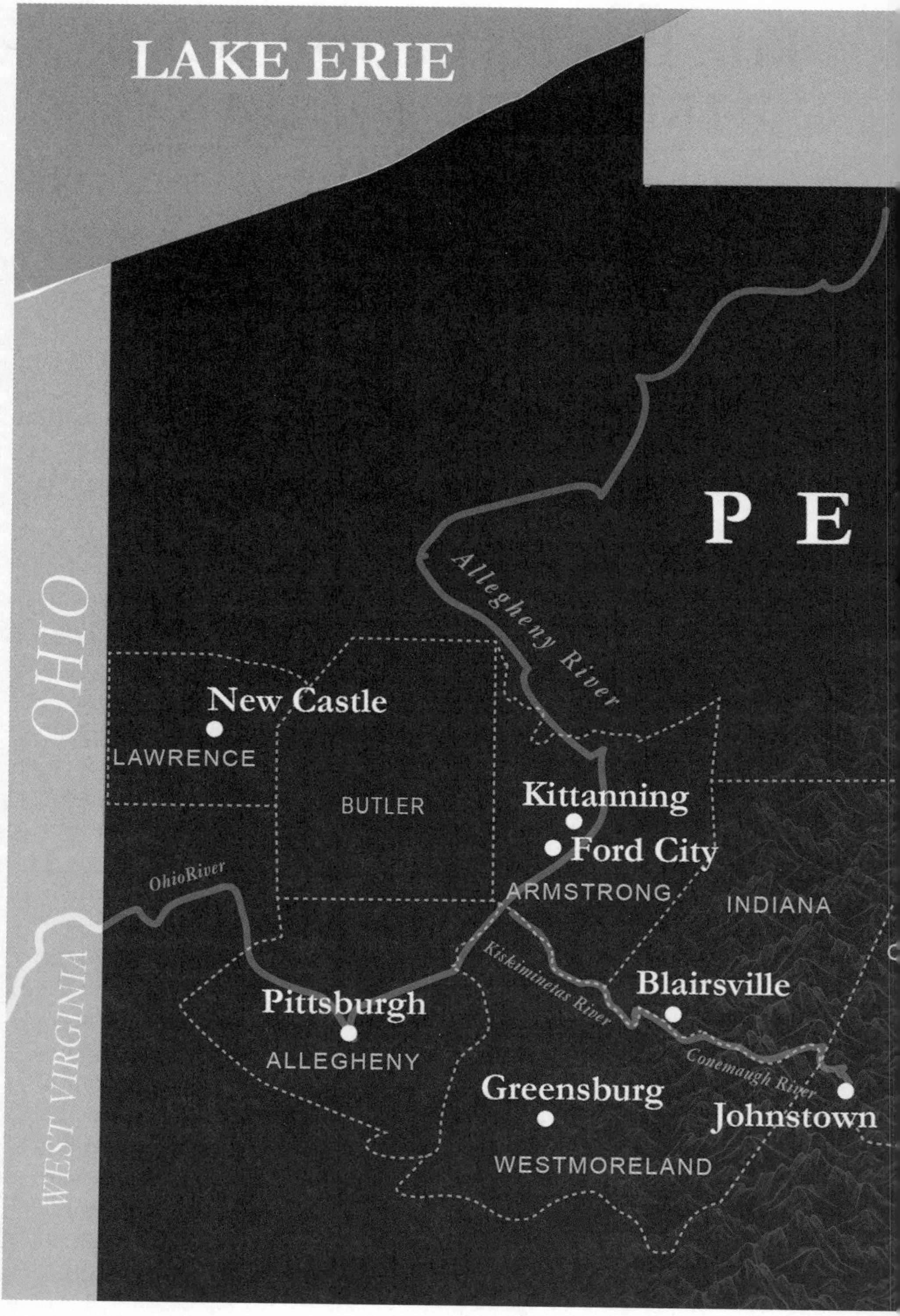

LAKE ERIE

OHIO

P E

Allegheny River

New Castle

LAWRENCE

BUTLER

Kittanning

Ford City

ARMSTRONG

INDIANA

OhioRiver

WEST VIRGINIA

Kiskiminetas River

Blairsville

Pittsburgh

ALLEGHENY

Conemaugh River

Greensburg

Johnstown

WESTMORELAND

NEW YORK

NSYLVANIA

Tyrone

Huntingdon Furnace

Juniata River

Altoona

Huntingdon

Foot of Ten

BLAIR

Path
Valley

Harrisburg

Hollidaysburg

Orbisonia

Susquehanna
River

HUNTINGDON

The things that truly last
When view and times have passed,
They are all in Pennsylvania this morning.

—Rudyard Kipling

CHAPTER 1

THE PATHBREAKERS: CAPTAIN THOMAS BLAIR AND JOHN BLAIR

I could not help taking a more extensive view of the vast
inland navigation of these United States . . . and could not
but be struck by the immense extent and importance of
it, and of the goodness of that Providence which has dealt
its favors to us with so profuse a hand. Would to God we
may have wisdom enough to improve them. I shall not rest
contented till I have explored the Western country, and
traversed those lines, or great part of them, which have
given bounds to a new empire."

—George Washington,
in a letter to the Marquis de Chastellux, 1783

In the years following the Revolution, when the new United States
of America looked toward a future made boundless by freedom, a
man in Pennsylvania surveyed the landscape of his own life. Captain
Thomas Blair had already lived fifty years, though he hardly felt a day
of it. His health was sound and his body strong. He had been blessed with
a family and work enough to prosper. He had served in the French and
Indian campaigns and then fought for independence from the Crown. By
any measure, he'd done much with what he had been given, yet he wanted
to do more.

He had seen new, untouched land during his service to the Patriot
cause. That land was calling him, three hundred forested acres of it, in a
water gap along the eastern edge of Allegheny Mountain, that great sentry
of the Ohio Country beyond. He and his family left their home in Path
Valley and settled at the mouth of the gap among the sycamores, just a
stone's throw from the gushing stream. They built a log homestead and
cleared ground for farming. In a few years' time, they had built a pair of

gristmills and a distillery. It was the kind of place a man could enjoy living out the rest of his days, this place known forever after as Blair's Gap.

Meanwhile, about thirty miles from the Gap, the first iron furnace in the Juniata River Valley went into blast. Captain Blair and his son were quick to understand how important ironmaking was to the Juniata Valley, so they went about doing what most people said couldn't be done: creating a shipping route to move iron and other Juniata-made goods over the Alleghenies to the burgeoning West. What began as a rough track scratched into local dirt for their fellow settlers became the path forward for an enterprising American family and a nation eager to see what it could make of itself.

The Blairs' story actually began an ocean away in the province of Ulster, a region comprised of nine counties in present-day Ireland and Northern Ireland. In the seventeenth century, many Lowland families emigrated from Scotland and settled on land made inexpensive by King James I, who was encouraging the relocation of Protestant Scots to Ulster for political purposes. Though the hardworking Scots-Irish made the region a great economic success, hundreds of thousands of families left Ulster for America and other British colonies during the 1700s. Some crossed the Atlantic to seek relief from a series of crippling droughts and rising rents, while others sought freedom from religious persecution.

The man who genealogists would identify as "John Blair of Fannett Township" left Ulster with his family and arrived in Pennsylvania around 1734. While the reason for the Blairs' immigration is not known, genealogical records suggest they made the journey with a family named McClelland and members of the Holliday family, whose descendants would establish Hollidaysburg, Pennsylvania. The Blairs made their home in Path Valley, a settlement in present-day Franklin County.

In 1755, while Pennsylvania was still a colony under British rule, John Blair served in British Major General Braddock's failed campaign to capture Fort Duquesne from the French. John's son, Thomas, enlisted for military service in 1759 at the age of twenty-six and fought in the French and Indian War, earning the rank of Captain. Thomas's brother, Alexander, also served and was killed at Fort Venango in 1763 while he was still a young man.

Thomas Blair was, to his very bones, a patriot. In the pivotal years of the Revolution that followed the signing of the Declaration of Independence,

Captain Thomas Blair, 3rd Company, 2nd Battalion of the Pennsylvania Militia, fought on the American frontier. Though it was not a battlefront for any formal military campaigns, central Pennsylvania was nonetheless a contested place during the Revolution. There were nearly as many Tories— those who remained loyal to Great Britain—in the upper Juniata Valley as there were Patriots. Tory leaders promised payment for prisoners and scalps; whether those scalps belonged to Patriot men, women, or children made little difference. As a result, the volunteer Patriot militia was tasked with defending settlements and families from attacks by Tories and their Native American allies, often with bloody consequences.

In 1778, Major Cluggage of the Continental Army received word that well-known Tory John Weston was assembling a heavily-armed band of men at Kittanning with plans to march through the river valleys of central Pennsylvania to Lancaster, seizing property and killing all Patriots he encountered along the way. Cluggage was overseeing the construction of a fort, which would later be named Fort Roberdeau, in Sinking Valley. His duty was to protect a crucial lead mining and smelting operation, so he could not leave his post to address the Tory threat. Cluggage sent Captain Thomas Blair instead. In just forty-eight hours, Captain Blair assembled thirty-five men to stop Weston's march. Twenty of the men were from Captain Blair's hometown of Path Valley, and the rest came from either Frankstown or Standing Stone, a settlement that would be renamed Huntingdon.

In the account written by U.J. Jones in 1855, Captain Blair led his rangers "with great vigor" over the Allegheny Ridge on the Kittanning Path (also known as the Frankstown Path). Where the trail crossed the headwaters of Blacklick Creek, the group came upon two Tories. Blair's men were eager to shoot, but Captain Blair intervened and spared their lives. The Tories reported that Weston and his plot were no more. Weston and about ten of his men had been killed when others in the group turned on Weston after suspecting a set-up. With their leader fallen, Weston's band dispersed. Had Captain Blair allowed his men to kill the Tories upon sight, they would have missed crucial information and continued their mission needlessly. That night, despite the rain and dwindling provisions, the men celebrated their good fortune; they would begin their march for home in the morning.

At dawn, two guides set out in search of game for breakfast, but they never returned. Their trail showed signs that they had been taken prisoner. Fearing an ambush, Blair's men started their homeward march. They endured days upon days of rain, vicious hunger, and sickness. They eventually made it home without losing a man, but their work hunting Tories wasn't over. They stopped at the home of another known Tory in Pleasant Valley, and though they tied him to a "hickory sapling and fastened the branches of it around his neck, and at a given signal, let him swing," Blair's men took mercy on the man before he was seriously injured. He renounced his loyalty to the British Crown and was permitted to join the rangers.

A similar story recounts how Blair's rangers from Path Valley once hunted a "notorious" Tory named Jacob Hare. The men believed what they had heard about Hare's unwavering support of the British and his trademark brutality. Drunk on a sense of justice—and perhaps some whiskey too—they paid Hare a visit. By the time Captain Blair arrived, his men were preparing to hang Hare from a rafter in his log house. With some convincing, Captain Blair was able to stop them from carrying out the execution, though one of the men did *cut both [Hare's] ears off close to his head!* Despite Captain Blair's belief in mercy, the frontier of the Revolution was often an unforgiving place.

At the end of his service in the Pennsylvania militia, Captain Blair's contribution to the Juniata Valley and his country was just beginning. When the family settled at the mouth of Blair's Gap situated about four miles west of present-day Hollidaysburg, there were no well-established travel routes in the valley except for "Indian paths" like the Kittanning Path, which were cut for the passage of just one or a few people at a time. And then there were the Alleghenies themselves, which stood as a formidable barrier to all points west. There was talk among the newcomers, including Captain Blair and his son, John, about creating a packhorse track for travel over the ridge. The early settlers scoffed at the idea; after all, they had been petitioning the county for roads for over a decade, but to no avail. Building a road just couldn't be done, they said. But the Blairs believed otherwise.

Captain Blair knew the land well. John was also a keen observer and a quick study of his father's example. With the help of other intrepid neighbors, they succeeded in cutting a packhorse route through Blair's Gap up and over the Alleghenies. Though this first road was just wide enough for one man and a horse loaded down with goods, the path was a precursor to greater transportation improvements on the horizon, improvements that would transform the Juniata region and spur the industrial destiny of the nation.

In 1785, shortly after the Blairs settled in Blair's Gap, George Ashman—who had been one of Thomas Blair's commanding officers during the Revolution—

and his partners set up Bedford Furnace near present-day Orbisonia. It was the first furnace in the Juniata ironmaking region, an area encompassing all or parts of present-day Perry, Juniata, Mifflin, Centre, Huntingdon, Blair, and Bedford counties. During the 1790s, ironmaking in the Juniata region took off. The name "Juniata Charcoal Iron" became synonymous with superior quality. In a letter to a friend dated 1819, entrepreneur, inventor, and manufacturer Eli Whitney spoke highly of Juniata iron:

> About ten or twelve years ago I purchased at Columbia,
> Pennsylvania, about 15 tons of the common Juniata Iron . . .
> which was wrought, in my manufactory, into various parts of
> muskets. From my own observation & experience, I am satisfied
> that the Juniata Metal, in its native state, is some of the best in
> the world & that if it is carefully & skillfully manufactured, it will
> answer an excellent purpose for musket Barrels or any other use.

In a sense, Juniata iron had to be excellent. With no adequate shipping routes by land or water, transporting the iron products out of the valley was difficult and costly. Therefore, the value of the goods had to justify the trouble of moving them. To reach eastern markets, Juniata ironmasters, millers, farmers, and other producers loaded their goods into temporary wooden boats called arks and rafted them down the Juniata River to the Susquehanna. This was possible only when the water levels in local streams were high enough, usually in early spring following the winter melt and a good rain. Once an ark reached its destination, it was dismantled for lumber.

To ship their products westward, including to Pittsburgh, ironmasters would either load down wagons or bend bar iron into a U shape and hang the bars over the backs of horses and mules for the long trek over the Alleghenies. The difficult terrain, exposure to the elements, and sheer distance was hard on both the drivers and their animals. There was no way to expedite the journey or make it less physically demanding, since drivers had to "shift the cargo" off the animals periodically so as not to exhaust them.

The Blairs welcomed the drivers to stay at the family home when they passed through Blair's Gap. The family offered a rest, a meal, and conversation over spirits and ale. John Blair listened to the drivers' stories of their long and treacherous journeys, tales replete with black gnats, rattlesnakes, thunderstorms, and sucking mud. Though a packhorse track was an improvement on wilderness trails, John Blair knew there had to be a better way. He knew, too, that manufacturers and merchants in the

East were eager to get their products into the expanding West, which was opening further to settlement each day. He knew the hardworking ironmasters of the Juniata Valley could meet settlers' need for wagon wheels, tools, and other goods, and Juniata farmers had produce to spare. Improving transportation routes for Juniata goods became his mission.

From an early age, John Blair took a deep interest in law and civic matters, and just like his father, he became a person who made things happen. In 1791, he launched into public service as a county commissioner of newly formed Huntingdon County.

In 1792, while John Blair was living in Huntingdon, Michael Cryder, the owner of a gristmill near Huntingdon, and two of his sons piloted an ark carrying 104 barrels of flour on the Susquehanna River, over the Conewago Falls, through Chesapeake Bay, and into Baltimore. The Cryders were the first to successfully navigate the falls, which had proven to be too perilous for all other ark and keel boat pilots. Upon their arrival, merchants paid Michael Cryder a premium price for his flour. They recognized that the Juniata miller had accomplished something extraordinary.

John Blair, too, was impressed. Like the grit he had admired in the packhorse drivers who braved Allegheny Mountain, Cryder's feat inspired Blair to consider other ways to improve transportation through the Juniata Valley. In 1807, the state of Pennsylvania appointed commissioners to begin issuing stock for a turnpike road from Harrisburg to Pittsburgh that would run through Lewistown and Huntingdon. Few believed in the feasibility of the project, and it was not funded.

In autumn of 1810, Captain Thomas Blair died at the age of seventy-six. He was considered "a real pioneer, patriot, valiant soldier, and a valuable citizen"—a man who had earned great respect in his lifetime. In his later years, Captain Blair served as an elder of the First Presbyterian Church at Hollidaysburg and was named one of the township officers of Frankstown Township. Though Captain Blair "had no conception of the part he was playing in the birth of a nation," his contributions would reach far beyond Blair's Gap.

In January 1814, those Huntingdon County citizens still in favor of a turnpike road met at the courthouse. Among those leaders was John Blair, who helped petition the State Legislature to use a portion of the funds that had already been raised to continue plans for a turnpike across the Alleghenies. The proposed route would begin east of the mountains at the Blair family homestead where John Blair now lived; it would go over the mountains, pass through Munster and Ebensburg, and end at Martin

Reager's tavern on the west side of Laurel Hill. Ultimately, the turnpike road would start in Blair's Gap and end in a settlement on the Conemaugh River about forty miles west of Pittsburgh. Later, when the settlement was officially recognized, it was named Blairsville to honor the man who made the road happen.

John Blair served as the president of the Huntingdon, Cambria and Indiana Turnpike Company from 1815 until 1826. In the early days of construction, he was often spotted along the route astride his trusty horse, observing the project's progress. Much of his role was to keep the project funded. When cash ran short, the company issued "shinplasters" that operated like paper money. The notes were negotiable and exchanged among buyers and sellers for goods and services. Holders could eventually cash in the shinplasters for their value in currency.

Although it was more like a narrow wagon trail than the wide, paved highways we know today, the Huntingdon, Cambria, and Indiana Turnpike Road was a major improvement in transportation. Records from the Blairsville terminal of the turnpike in 1829 show an impressive amount of traffic, including 4,372 single horses, 781 four-horse wagons, 730 stagecoaches, 1,566 five-horse teams, 497 cattle, 475 swine, and 12,527 foot passengers. This turnpike road would eventually become part of the William Penn Highway, also known as US Route 22.

Not long after the turnpike road opened in 1819, John Blair became involved in another transportation project: the Pennsylvania Canal system. The state of New York was building the Erie Canal to connect the Hudson River to Lake Erie, and businessmen in Philadelphia and Pittsburgh— and visionaries like John Blair in between— knew that to compete, Pennsylvania would have to create its own route that would facilitate trade with the growing West. At first, the commission of representatives from Pennsylvania's counties proposed the creation of a continuous waterway from Philadelphia to Pittsburgh. The plan would require cutting a four-mile tunnel through the Allegheny Mountains, a project deemed too costly. Instead, the commission conceived a 395-mile statewide system of canals and roads and later railroads that would transport goods and travelers from one end of the state to the other.

Work on the "Main Line of Public Works" began in Harrisburg in 1826. John Blair rejoined the Pennsylvania General Assembly to put himself in a better position to advocate for the Juniata Division, the portion of the canal that would pass through Huntingdon County. Frankstown was the natural place for the western terminus of the Juniata Division, but after a farmer refused to sell his land where the canal basin needed to be built, Blair convinced the commission to site the terminus in Hollidaysburg instead.

Work began on the Juniata Division of the canal in 1827, and by 1829, passenger boats were using the waterway. Canal boats held about fifty passengers and were pulled along by horses on dry-land towpaths at four miles per hour. Still, crowds gathered to marvel at the new mode of transportation. The Main Line was billed as a "fast new service" with a "low toll." Prior to the canals, it took twenty-three days to travel from Philadelphia to Pittsburgh; the Main Line could get a person there in five.

In the spring of 1831, construction began on the Allegheny Portage Railroad, a carefully engineered system of stationary engines, horse teams, inclined planes, pulleys, and rope to haul freight and passengers between the Juniata Division of the Pennsylvania Canal in Hollidaysburg and the Western Division of the canal in Johnstown. There were a total of ten inclined planes—five on one side of the mountain and five on the other—numbered 1 through 10 from west to east. Upon arriving by boat in Hollidaysburg on the east side of the mountain or in Johnstown on the west, these "section boats" were disassembled into two or four pieces, loaded onto carts, and pulled along the inclined planes up to the mountain summit and down the other side. Likewise, passengers would disembark from their canal boats and make the trip over the mountain in designated railcars—1,398 feet up from Hollidaysburg and 1,171 feet down into Johnstown, and vice versa.

On March 18, 1834, the Portage Railroad was open for operation. This stretch of thirty-six miles between Hollidaysburg and Johnstown, added to the eighty-two miles of state railroad from Philadelphia to Columbia and the Eastern, Juniata, and Western Divisions of the canal, officially completed Pennsylvania's Main Line. From 1832 to 1835, Hollidaysburg grew from a small village of 30 houses and fewer than 100 residents into a town of more than 1,200 people eager to work and do business. Thanks to traffic from the canal and the Portage Railroad, it was considered one of the most prosperous towns between Philadelphia and Pittsburgh.

John Blair did live to see the Pennsylvania Canal in operation. In November 1829, he and other members of the General Assembly from western counties rode on the "Juniata," the first packet boat to travel the Juniata Division of the canal. As one observer wrote, the boat "was drawn by two white horses when she set off in fine style, with the 'star-spangled banner' flying at her head, and amidst the roar of cannon, the shouts of the populace, and the cheering music of the band which was on board." John Blair did not live to see the opening of the canal in his own neck of the woods, however. In January 1832, he died at home in Blair's Gap. Later that year, on November 28, 1832, at ten o'clock in the morning, the packet boat "John Blair" left Huntingdon for Hollidaysburg, officially opening the canal route between the two towns. In the year following, the port of Huntingdon would see 3,000 tons of merchandise in transit.

Not twenty years later, canal travel was considered "a slow coach." Though the hybrid transportation system—part waterway, part railway—was an engineering marvel, the expanding railroad industry was rapidly overtaking it. Railroads had several advantages over canals. Not only were they less costly to build and maintain, but railroads could operate in the winter while canals could not. Railroads were simply faster and more efficient. By 1852, the Pennsylvania Railroad (PRR) completed its all-rail line from Philadelphia to Pittsburgh, and Hollidaysburg was replaced as a key commercial hub by a new railroad town called Altoona. With the completion of the Horseshoe Curve in 1854, the PRR had managed to find quite literally a way around the Allegheny Mountains and render the Portage Railroad unnecessary.

In 1855, the state of Pennsylvania attempted to sell the Main Line transportation system without success. Two years later, the PRR bought the Main Line for $7.5 million dollars—$2.5 million below the original sale price—and ran the system for a few months before shutting it down and reassigning its most useful parts to the railroad.

Author and Huntingdon native U.J. Jones observed how impressed the public seemed to be with steam engines and rail travel and, with remarkable foresight, warned his readers about the ever-changing nature of technology:

> Let us not glory too much over the demon scream of the
> locomotive as it comes rattling through the valley, belching
> forth fire and smoke, or the miraculous telegraph which
> conveys messages from one end of the Union to the other with
> the rapidity with which a lover's sigh would be wafted from
> the Indies to the Pole; for who knows but that the succeeding
> generation, following in the footsteps made by the universal
> law of progress, will astonish the world with inventions not
> dreamed of in our philosophy, which will throw our electric-
> telegraphs and railroads forever in the shade?

Beginning with the packhorse route in the late 1780s and continuing through the construction of the Pennsylvania Canal and Portage Railroad, transportation in the Juniata Valley was transformed completely during the lifetimes of Captain Thomas Blair and John Blair. As a result, the Valley itself underwent a transformation. What began as a wild frontier dotted with forts, trading posts, and small settlements grew into a network of population centers bustling with industry and commerce connected to each other by roads, waterways, and rails. Hollidaysburg and its surrounding area had grown so much that in 1846 a new county was formed from parts of Huntingdon and Bedford counties. It was named for the son of a pioneer who was himself a pioneer, a man who made it his life's work to go down the road less traveled—and create one out of dust if he had to. Perhaps no other person of that era deserved the honor of having a county named for him more than John Blair. In 1946, Blair County celebrated its centennial.

Musing on the scope and significance of John Blair's life, writer M.A. Miller imagined the pathbreaker in the borough of Huntingdon, the launching place for so many of his undertakings. Miller envisioned John Blair standing behind the courthouse that Blair himself had planned and financed, looking out across the Juniata River and remembering Indian canoes and Cryder's ark. It was there that Blair gained the support to lead the Huntingdon, Cambria and Indian Turnpike Road Company and advocate for the Juniata Division of the canal. It was in Huntingdon that Blair "caught the vision of providing transportation lanes, the triumph of which helped build a nation."

John Blair and Captain Thomas Blair both had extraordinary vision for what was possible, especially when others were convinced that the pitfalls outweighed the potential gains. Their descendants would encounter some of the same obstacles—changing technologies, economic uncertainty, the growing pains of a young country—albeit in different times and on different terrain. For succeeding generations of Blairs, the path laid by their forefathers was an admirable one to follow. But at every turn, the legacies of Captain Thomas Blair and John Blair were also a command to break from the given path and lead the way in a new direction, toward something untested and unknown.

CHAPTER 2

IRON AGE: THE BLAIRS AND SHOENBERGERS

There he lived, this Iron Master, iron in his fibre; iron in his
eye; iron in his waking moments; iron at night with
the Furnace fires shining in his windows. The leader of
these strong loyal pioneers.

—Mary Wigton Reeve,
Iron Furnace Baronies of Huntingdon County

In 1797, the year John Blair completed his courthouse, Thomas S.
Blair was born in the borough of Huntingdon. As the first son of John
Blair and the namesake of Captain Thomas Blair, the boy grew up in
the shadows of two enterprising and widely admired men. But young
Thomas had his own well of ambition and independence to draw from.
He studied law, passed the bar in Huntingdon, and then plotted his own
course. Before he was twenty, he left his family and moved a hundred miles
westward to Armstrong County.

Kittanning was still a frontier town when Thomas arrived around
1815. He established his law practice and quickly became a successful and
respected lawyer in the area. He was a captain in the Armstrong Guards, a
volunteer military organization organized following the War of 1812 and
served on committees that promoted the interests of Armstrong County
residents and businesses. In 1821 he married Miss Florinda Cust of
Greensburg, Pennsylvania. The couple had two sons together and enjoyed
a comfortable life among Kittanning's gentry.

In 1837, at thirty-nine years old, Thomas S. Blair died. Florinda Blair
moved her sons, only twelve and ten years old, and her widowed mother
to Pittsburgh to live with Florinda's younger sister, Maggie. Margaret Cust
Shoenberger was married to the prosperous iron manufacturer, John H.
Shoenberger, son of the Pennsylvania "Iron King," Dr. Peter Shoenberger.

It was this family connection that set the course for the life of Thomas and Florinda's younger son, Thomas Shoenberger Blair.

Young Thomas came of age in a time that was vibrating with technological innovation and invention driven by feverish westward expansion. If a place could be reached by river or rail or stagecoach (and even if it couldn't be), Americans and recently immigrated Americans were going there. There was wealth to be had, they knew, for the hardest worker, the smartest speculator, the first on the scene—it was only a matter of finding it. In the same way, if a problem presented itself, surely a solution existed, too—it was only a matter of finding it. Any obstacle was merely that: something to be scaled, surmounted, or simply pushed out of the way.

With this ethos, in this environment, Thomas Shoenberger Blair applied his wits and tenacity toward making steel. Just as his grandfather and great-grandfather had done when they sought to improve transportation through the Juniata Valley, he would attempt to do the thing that others said couldn't be done. In the end, Thomas Shoenberger Blair would know both success and failure. In the end, the Blair story would be one about American steel. But in the beginning, there was iron.

———

As early as 1607, European settlers were making iron in the American colonies. Artisans began with techniques they brought from the Old World, but with the freedom to experiment and a fresh supply of natural resources at their disposal, they could develop new ways of making the goods that were crucial to settlement and expansion. Ironmaking began on the Atlantic coast of the colonies but caught on in Pennsylvania thanks to the province's natural gifts. Its earth was rich in the key ingredient, iron ore, and quality limestone for fluxing. Its valleys were dense with forests for making the charcoal that fueled early furnaces and forges. Its running streams provided water power and shipping routes.

In 1716, a blacksmith named Thomas Rutter bought land not far from present-day Pottstown, believing the conditions were right for making iron. With his son-in-law, Rutter erected a bloomery forge along Manatawny Creek, a tributary of the Schuylkill River. In a bloomery forge, iron ore was heated and then hammered to separate the iron from other elements. The resulting ball of solid iron and liquid slag could then be further refined according to its end use. Rutter's operation was the first bloomery forge in Pennsylvania. Rutter soon realized a charcoal blast furnace would make iron of better quality and more efficiently than a bloomery could, and so with the backing of investors, he built Colebrookdale Furnace, the first iron furnace of its kind in the province.

Over the next few decades, furnaces and forges cropped up throughout the Schuylkill Valley. The success and growth of these ironworks and others in the Middle Atlantic region prompted Britain to attempt to regulate the production and importation of American iron in 1750. The Iron Act was not well enforced, and by 1775, the American colonies were the third largest producer of iron in the world.

During the Revolution, American ironmasters made cannon, shot, and metal for other small arms. Upon gaining independence, the nation needed iron products for the explorers and settlers pushing westward. In 1787, the Northwest Ordinance opened the Ohio and Mississippi River basins to settlement, a development that further increased demand for transportation and building supplies, including carriage wheel rims and blacksmith tools. In 1810, the total national output of iron was about 54,000 tons per year. By 1840, the total had more than quintupled to 286,000 tons.

The manufacture of iron and steel would become hallmarks of industrialization and urban life, but ironmaking started out as a rural enterprise and remained so for more than a century after Rutter's first ironworks was established on Pennsylvania soil. Until about 1840, most iron furnaces were fueled by charcoal, which was made by smoldering wood to the point it became almost pure carbon. Blanketed by hardwood forest and embedded with high-quality ore, the Juniata Valley was an ideal place to make iron.

By the early 1800s, Juniata ironworks were churning out pig iron and wrought iron in plantations all over the countryside. "Pig" and "pig iron" refer to the cast iron ingots produced from a blast furnace. The terms are thought to be the result of creative visual interpretation: In a charcoal-fueled furnace, molten ore was drawn down to the sand floor where it flowed into larger molds first and then filled smaller molds set perpendicular to the larger molds. The arrangement of the larger and smaller molds reminded workers of piglets suckling a sow. The iron cast into the smaller molds were "pigs," the iron from the larger molds were "sows," and together they were referred to as "pig iron." "Wrought iron" was the resulting material when pig iron was processed in a forge or a mill. Wrought iron was less brittle than pig iron and was easier to pound or roll into other forms.

At the center of the rural iron plantations was either the furnace stack or the forge. These structures were surrounded by buildings that serviced the ironmaking operation, including large sheds full of charcoal. Just beyond the central buildings sat the office and company store, and a short walk from it all were the cottages and boarding houses where the workers and their families lived.

Anywhere from twenty to sixty or seventy men, including some indentured servants and slaves, did the backbreaking work of keeping the ironworks producing around the clock, every day of the week, for months at a time. Certain workers, like founders, who kept the furnace in blast; molders, who drew the molten iron into molds; and colliers, who smoldered wood to make charcoal fuel, earned higher wages than woodcutters and teamsters.

For the workers and their families, ironmaking was much more than a livelihood; it was their whole world. They lived in company-owned housing. They ate food grown on company farmland, shopped at the company store, and went to services at the company church. Their children attended the company school if one was established and played in fields and forestland owned by the company.

Overseeing it all from the grandest house on the plantation "set well back from the public road and the too-inquiring eye of village denizen" was the ironmaster. He held undisputed authority over both the ironmaking operation and his workers. Because the universe of an iron plantation made for so little separation between work life and domestic life, some ironmasters assumed a patriarchal role. They demanded obedience from their workers, preached the virtue of industriousness, and imposed rules on social conduct. On the other side of the coin was an ironmaster's sense of responsibility for the welfare of his workers and their families. He relied on his workers' skill and diligence to keep the forge pounding and the furnace fire burning—work that was physically exhausting, dirty, and dangerous—and so, in the best situations, the ironmaster and his family did what they could to take care of their people.

During the heyday of charcoal-fueled furnaces (about 1790–1850), ironmaking was an extremely lucrative business for company owners in the Juniata region, though wealth and success were not guaranteed. Iron companies were usually comprised of a few stakeholders, including the owner of the land, a financial backer, and someone who had expertise in ironmaking. It was common for owners to buy into and sell out of these iron companies frequently and sometimes rapidly, in pursuit of the next promising investment opportunity.

Few ironmasters had more success than Dr. Peter Shoenberger. The "Iron King of Pennsylvania" had a Midas touch when it came to making iron. But it wasn't a gift from the gods of iron. Dr. Shoenberger's furnaces and forges were some of the most productive and most profitable in the Commonwealth because of his meticulous—some would say obsessive—management of every part of the ironmaking process.

Peter Shoenberger's father, George, was among the many German immigrants who settled in Lancaster County, Pennsylvania, and applied their knowledge to the American iron industry. In 1800, George Shoenberger was part of John Gloninger & Co., the company that operated Huntingdon Furnace on Warrior's Mark Run. By 1803, he was the ironmaster of the furnace. In 1804, with partner Dr. Samuel Fahnestock, George Shoenberger built the Juniata Forge on the Little Juniata River.

Young Peter Shoenberger spent his boyhood among iron furnaces and forges in the wilds of Huntingdon County, but his father encouraged him to explore Dr. Fahnestock's profession. Peter left home to study under his mentor and then began his medical practice. Whether Dr. Shoenberger had aspirations for a long career in medicine, we will never know, for fate had different plans. George Shoenberger died in 1815, and Peter assumed the management of Juniata Forge and Huntingdon Furnace. It was just the beginning for the man about whom Andrew Carnegie would say, "he was to the iron industry what I later would become to the steel industry."

Over the next forty years, Dr. Peter Shoenberger built or acquired several furnaces and forges throughout the Juniata Valley, many of which he named for his wife and daughters, a common practice among owners and ironmasters. To fuel his ironworks, he bought immense tracts of forestland. He controlled ore mines and later coal mines and was always hunting for new deposits. At one time, Dr. Shoenberger's land holdings totaled more than 100,000 acres. He traveled throughout Huntingdon, Blair, and Bedford counties, often on horseback, to keep a close eye on all his ironworks and supporting operations.

In 1824, Dr. Shoenberger built a rolling mill in Pittsburgh on the banks of the Allegheny River between 15th and 16th Streets. The Juniata Iron Works processed iron blooms into an array of products including boiler plates, horseshoes, and nails. The mill produced 800 tons of rolled iron in 1825 alone. After meeting Dr. Shoenberger on a stagecoach journey from Harrisburg to Carlisle and being sufficiently impressed with him, journalist, travel writer, and notoriously scathing muckraker Anne Royall agreed to visit "Dr. S.'s" Juniata Works. She was not disappointed. "This is the first great manufactory I was ever in," she wrote, and had I not been prepared for the sight and noise by seeing others upon a less scale, I should have thought it was the shop of Vulcan, forging his thunderbolts in his subterraneous abode. The redness of the towering flames, the amazing dimensions of the wheels, the volumes of rolling smoke, and the thunder of the huge hammers, and squeaking of the nail machines, fairly turned my head—no language can describe the rapidity with which these nails are made, they drop from the machine in one unremitting shower.

It is not surprising that an observer would be wowed by the mill's nail output. The mass production of nails was still a relatively novel concept, but it was a timely one for a nation that was growing as fast as manufacturers could pump out building materials. Iron, glass, brass, and tin all were being produced in Pittsburgh. For many pioneers, the city was the last stop for supplies before heading west. At the time Dr. Shoenberger established his Juniata Iron Works, there were only a few rolling mills in the city, but the future of the Shoenberger family business—and the future of ironmaking itself—would be in Pittsburgh.

Like all Juniata ironmasters, Dr. Shoenberger had to address the challenges of transporting his products out of central Pennsylvania. To supply his Pittsburgh mill with Juniata blooms, Shoenberger's wagon teams hauled loads over the Allegheny Front to the headwaters of the Conemaugh River at Johnstown and floated the iron on boats down the Kiskiminetas River, to the Allegheny River, and into the city.

The turnpike road used by Shoenberger's Juniata wagon teams was the same road lobbied for and financed by John Blair. Records from the Blair's Gap terminal of the turnpike show that in 1829 Dr. Shoenberger stayed at John Blair's home for several days on his way from Pittsburgh to points east. Though he often traveled through Blair's Gap, Dr. Shoenberger's visit was likely spurred by a desire to discuss the ongoing construction of the Juniata Division of the canal—of which John Blair was an outspoken champion and Dr. Shoenberger a significant investor—and plans for an inclined railroad over the mountains. Little did the men know that in a few years' time they would be relatives by marriage and their families would become more closely tied than either could have imagined.

By the early 1830s, the Iron King of Pennsylvania had built quite a kingdom. He was the first iron manufacturer to own the entire supply chain, from the mines that provided fuel for his iron furnaces (many of which were beginning to use bituminous coal or coke instead of charcoal) to the rolling mills and transportation systems of finished goods. His company was called "P. Shoenberger & Son" to acknowledge the involvement of earnest, intelligent John Hopson Shoenberger, who joined the family business in Pittsburgh after completing college. In 1836, John and his older brother, George, succeeded their father as the firm "G. and J.H. Shoenberger." Soon after, Dr. Shoenberger and his wife, Sarah, deeded a large portion of their holdings to their sons and daughters, including 25,000 acres of land in Huntingdon and Centre counties.

Even after securing his legacy, Dr. Shoenberger was not the kind of ruler to sit idly upon his throne. Among his many investments and manufacturing ventures, he built the first rolling mill in Wheeling (at that time still part of Virginia) and in 1852 was one of the founding members of the Cambria Iron Company in Johnstown, Pennsylvania. The company's rail mill would become one of the largest in the nation in the late 1850s, but Dr. Shoenberger ended his involvement with the company in 1854. He died later that year in Marietta, Pennsylvania, at the age of seventy-two, leaving an estate totaling more than $5 million—more than 150 million in today's dollars.

Far from a spoiled heir, John H. Shoenberger approached his role as custodian of the Shoenberger fortune with dignity and sincerity. After all, he was maintaining more than just material wealth; he was also upholding his father's life's work and name. John had grown up studying Peter, observing how masterfully he ran every facet of his business, how he could almost smell a seam of iron ore, how his rolling mill rained profit in the form of nails, and how skillfully he used that staggering wealth to generate even more. John saw how his father suffered neither fools nor loafers yet treated his workers and associates fairly. And, in certain moments to certain people, Peter was known to give his favor—and his money—freely.

John remained in Pittsburgh for the rest of his working life. He became a respected figure in manufacturing, banking, and philanthropy. Though he had no children of his own, he filled two crucial roles in the life of a young man who was like a son to him. The boy was a born thinker, and John H. Shoenberger would help him build upon those gifts he'd been given and make his mark upon an entire industry.

CHAPTER 3

MASTERING IRON, TAMING STEEL: THE WORK OF THOMAS SHOENBERGER BLAIR

The chief distinction of Pittsburgh is not smoke, and it
never was. . . . and even when smoke hung thick over
the city for a century it was accepted stoically and almost
affectionately as the life-sign of its prosperity. Instead,
the chief distinction of Pittsburgh is work.

—Franklin Toker,
Pittsburgh: An Urban Portrait

T he natural world fascinated young Thomas Shoenberger Blair.
He spent hours wandering among the white oaks, chestnuts,
and hickories, deep in thought about the whys and hows of
nature, leaving the hillside forests above the Allegheny River
only to make it home in time for the evening meal. Of course there was
school to attend because his father, a lawyer, and his mother, an educated
gentlewoman, demanded it. Not that he minded. If the outdoors were his
first home, then books were his second. He read easily and well, and it
wouldn't be long before he would begin studying Latin, just like his older
brother John.

One evening in late winter, just a few months after his tenth birthday,
Thomas returned from a happy afternoon tromping through the muddy
woods to find his mother stricken white and their cook in tears. Thomas's
father—strong, intelligent, admired—had died. Soon Thomas, John, his
mother, and grandmother left Kittanning and moved to Pittsburgh to live
with Aunt Maggie and Uncle John Shoenberger. Thomas adored his aunt,

who was so young and cheerful, and his uncle, who stood tall and solid like the black walnuts in the river bottom back home. The Shoenbergers had always cared for him and John more like sons than nephews. After all, John had been named for their uncle, and Thomas was given their last name for his middle name. But things would be different, he knew. Though they shared the Allegheny, Pittsburgh was a far cry from Kittanning. It would be a whole new world to study and explore.

Thomas Shoenberger Blair's formal education began at age twelve when he attended boarding school at the Episcopal Institute in Pittsburgh. At sixteen, he enrolled at Western University, the institution that would be renamed the University of Pittsburgh in 1908. By his senior year, there were only fourteen other students in his class. By graduation, he was the sole member of the class of 1843.

Though he'd earned his bachelor of arts, Thomas wanted to confirm that he was worthy of the degree. He entered Harvard College in the autumn of 1843 and spent one academic year there. He studied philosophy and political economy, earning high distinction for the latter subject when he graduated. The influence of his family, and particularly the legacy of his father, no doubt had a hand in steering Thomas's educational course. As part of his commencement exercises at Harvard, he gave a formal presentation called "Disquisition: The Influence of the Legal Profession in the United States." If only Thomas S. Blair, Esq., had been alive to hear it.

Throughout his formal schooling, Thomas's fascination with the natural world remained. There was a vibrant network of social clubs at Harvard, but the only one Thomas belonged to during his brief time there was the Natural History Society. When he came down with typhoid fever he became acquainted with Dr. Jeffries Wyman, a physician who would go on to do important work as a naturalist, anatomist, and anthropologist. Dr. Wyman became a friend and mentor to Thomas. The pair would discuss ideas and share observations in conversation and in letters for the next thirty years.

After Harvard, a career was waiting for Thomas back in Pittsburgh. He joined his Uncle John, who led the firm of G. and J.H. Shoenberger & Co., the continuation of the empire started by Dr. Peter Shoenberger. But how the industry had changed since the Iron King first began his reign. By 1840, charcoal was no longer the dominant fuel for making pig iron.

Ironmasters in Eastern Pennsylvania had discovered that anthracite furnaces were more efficient and cost effective to operate. In Western Pennsylvania, rich bituminous coal seams supplied coal cake or "coke" as an attractive (that is, cheaper) alternative to charcoal.

As a result of the changes in fuel and technology, the organization and culture of the iron industry also changed. Instead of making and forging their products in remote iron plantations, ironmasters began to integrate their furnaces and rolling mills in large production facilities near population centers like Pittsburgh. These large operations required much more capital and manpower than traditional charcoal-fueled ironworks, necessarily changing the way companies were owned and managed. Partnerships morphed into corporations, and the gap in power and pay between managers and employees widened. The model of ironmasters living and working alongside their workers was dissolving. The wealthy businessmen who owned the biggest iron furnaces and rolling mills of the time, members of the so-called "Pig Iron Aristocracy," lived physically apart—and quite differently—from their employees.

During his visit to the US in 1842, the British novelist Charles Dickens traveled on the Main Line Canal across Pennsylvania, up and over the Alleghenies on the Portage Railroad, and spent a few days in Pittsburgh. One source claims the Shoenbergers entertained Dickens during his stay. Dickens doesn't mention them in the book he wrote about his experience, initially titled *American Notes for General Circulation*. He does, however, remark on the comparison of Pittsburgh with a town in England well known for its industrial flavor, in his unsparing way: "Pittsburg is like Birmingham in England, at least its townspeople say so. Setting aside the streets, the shops, the houses, waggons, factories, public buildings, and population, perhaps it may be. It certainly has a great quantity of smoke hanging about it, and is famous for its ironworks." Dickens's lack of excitement over Pittsburgh's self-styled identity as a manufacturing powerhouse echoed the attitude held by iron manufacturers across Europe and the United Kingdom: the young American iron industry couldn't hold a candle to the long-established ironmasters across the Atlantic. But before long, American steelmakers would catch up.

Thomas Blair began his ironmaking career in the operations department at the Shoenbergers' Juniata Works around 1844. At the time, the firm's most lucrative products included nails, horseshoes, and wire. In addition to their healthy iron business, the Shoenberger brothers experimented with the production of blister and crucible steel. Steel was superior to iron for some applications, but early techniques like blister and crucible steelmaking were inefficient and inconsistent, not to mention far too expensive to use on a large scale. If US manufacturers needed quality steel in quantity, they still had to import it from Europe, for a price.

Thomas could hardly get close enough to the process of making metal. It wasn't the brutal art of rolling, pounding, and slitting the pig iron that fascinated him. It was the precise alchemy of elements that made a material what it was. He observed and pondered the chemical properties of iron like he had examined the trees and wildlife in the forests of his boyhood, like he had immersed himself in his studies at Western and Harvard. He wasn't just a scholar of manufacturing; he was a maker, always testing, probing, pressing the science to find a way to refine iron such that it retained its hardness but also became more malleable and flexible like steel.

Aside from his work for the Shoenbergers, Thomas developed other partnerships. Around 1850, he went into business with Colonel Samuel McKelvey, a fellow Pittsburgher who would earn his rank after volunteering for military service and becoming indispensable to the Union army during the Civil War. As the firm McKelvey & Blair Cast-Steel and File Manufacturing Company, the partners were some of the first manufacturers in Pittsburgh to produce quality cast steel in relatively large quantities. Cast steel was a product made using the crucible process, which involved melting iron in a vessel with carbon and pouring it into molds. Cast and crucible steel were different from "blister steel," which was produced by wrapping strips of iron in carbon, heating the strips for days so the iron could absorb the carbon, and then hammering out the slag. The resulting product got its name from the blisters that appeared on the surface of the iron due to the gas released during the process. McKelvey and Blair had earned their reputation as pioneers in cast steel production by 1852, but their business lasted only a couple of years.

In the 1850s, many manufacturers and inventors were experimenting with refining iron into steel. As early as 1847, a furnace manager in Kentucky named William Kelly began tinkering with methods for making wrought iron faster and with lower fuel costs. His experiments with pneumatic steelmaking—the process of refining iron by blasting air through it— eventually yielded "run-out metal," a product that was *almost* steel but not quite. Later, some would claim for their own benefit that Kelly was the first to discover pneumatic steelmaking; however, it was an English inventor whose name would become synonymous with a major breakthrough in the steel world. And to think it happened virtually by accident.

While working on a commission to develop a new kind of gun metal for the French military in 1854, Henry Bessemer let "a little more air" into his iron furnace to get the fire going. Later, he noticed that two pieces of pig iron had not fused with the other metal. Instead, those pieces had become "thin shells of decarburized iron," which made him wonder if air alone could convert iron into a malleable metal with reduced carbon content—essentially, steel. The real genius of his discovery was proving that a fuel-gobbling furnace was not necessary for converting crude iron into steel. Instead, the process could happen in a Bessemer converter, a vessel that held the molten iron while air burned out excess carbon and impurities. Bessemer's method meant it was now possible to make steel relatively quickly, cheaply, and in large quantities.

As important to his commercial success as the discovery itself were Bessemer's business savvy and knack for publicity. He was quick to show off his invention and give talks to influential figures and groups in the industry. He placed lengthy pieces about his process in London newspapers and hired writers to compose articles for trade magazines. In 1856 Bessemer was granted a US patent for his process. He knew it was far from perfected, but he marketed it as flawless nonetheless. He used funds from his previous successful inventions to build himself a steel works in Sheffield, England, where he worked out the kinks of his process and had a steelmaking operation up and running by 1859.

Bessemer had plenty of competition in the industry, so his decision to retain full rights to his patent and offer a limited number of licenses for the use of his process proved to be another wise move. This didn't stop some entrepreneurs from attempting to find ways around paying royalties to Bessemer, including tapping William Kelly's knowledge of pneumatic steelmaking and perpetuating the story that his early experiments were proof that he was making steel prior to Bessemer. Over the next decade, inventors and engineers further developed and refined Bessemer's technology based on key metallurgical discoveries and market demand.

In America, no demand was greater or more consequential than that of the railroad industry. Driven by the nation's breakneck westward growth and the capitalistic obsession with accessing new markets, railroad companies laid tracks as fast as they could get the iron rails. During the first railroad-building boom from approximately 1865–1872, most rails were imported, but after Montour Iron Works in Danville, Pennsylvania, developed a better, less labor-intensive way of rolling iron bars into finished T-shaped rails around 1845, domestic production took off. In the ten-year span from 1855 to 1865, production of iron rails increased by 250 percent. Even the industrial demands of the Civil War hardly slowed the output of American-made rails.

Because wrought iron was a relatively soft material, the rails wore out quickly. Some heavily traveled sections needed replacing every few months. Railroad executives knew that steel was a harder, more durable material, but it was much too expensive to import and use on a large scale. This problem caught the attention of a young, Scotland-born American entrepreneur named Andrew Carnegie. At the age of twenty-nine, Carnegie had already worked his way up from telegraph boy to superintendent of the Pennsylvania Railroad's Western Division. He'd made a small fortune in oil and other investments and retired from the railroad. In the spring of 1865, he began a five-month tour of Europe to become "a well-rounded man of culture." Though it was meant to be a trip for pleasure, moneymaking opportunities were never far from Carnegie's mind.

While in London, Carnegie paid a visit to Thomas Dodds, an Englishman who had invented a process to manufacture iron rails capped with steel. During the Civil War, Carnegie had helped his former boss at the Pennsylvania Railroad, J. Edgar Thomson, install all-steel rails imported from Europe. Thomson thought the rails were worth the higher price because they lasted more than a year, but Thomson used the steel rails only on short connector tracks; the material was too brittle to handle the pounding they would take on mainline tracks. And so, Carnegie believed if he could buy the American rights to Dodds's patents, he might have a customer in Thomson. As it happened, Carnegie didn't have to buy anything from Dodds. The young inventor was so charmed by Carnegie that he gave the American businessman exclusive rights "without a shilling changing hands."

Meanwhile, back in the States, another inventor had already been granted a patent for "a rail having a steel surface for resisting wear without increased liability to fracture, and at so moderate an increase in cost as not to forbid its introduction into common use." The patent credited to Thomas S. Blair of Pittsburg, Pennsylvania on May 19, 1863—and reissued on December 1, 1863 with changes that addressed problems with earlier versions of the steel rail—describes a product much like the "doddized rail" Carnegie had won in London. It is unclear whether Carnegie attempted to buy rights to Blair's patent and was unsuccessful or that he recognized the value of having some engineering brainpower behind his new venture and saw Blair as an advantageous partner. In any case, the two men formed The American Steeled Rail Company in 1866; Thomas S. Blair served as president, with Andrew Carnegie as vice president.

In early 1867, the Pittsburgh company shipped samples of their product to Thomson at the Pennsylvania Railroad. Thomson was not impressed with the performance of the product and questioned the rails' safety when bearing heavy loads. In a letter to Carnegie, Thomson wrote: "The experiments made in relation to the strength of the Doddized Rails has so much impaired my confidence in this process that I didn't feel at liberty to increase our order for these rails . . . the process is not a success." Carnegie disregarded Thomson's remarks and continued to sell the merits of the rails to potential customers. Scientific mind that he was, Thomas Blair likely continued to experiment with improving the rails, but ultimately, they were not the viable product Carnegie and Blair hoped they would be. Angry customers returned the "steeled rails," Carnegie blamed Dodds for the faulty technology, and the American Steeled Rail Co. was dissolved soon after.

It was not the last the iron and steel industry would see of either Andrew Carnegie or Thomas S. Blair. Though their steeled rail venture was not a success, Carnegie and Blair were right about the metal. Steel was about to become the lifeblood of the railroads. In 1867, the same year that Carnegie and Blair abandoned their steeled rail project, the first all-steel rails in the US were produced by the Pennsylvania Railroad-owned Pennsylvania Steel Company near Harrisburg, and the first steel rails rolled on order were manufactured at the Cambria Iron Works—the company formed by Dr. Peter Shoenberger fourteen years earlier. In 1880, only 29 percent of the 115,000 miles of track in America were steel rail, but in just ten years' time, half of the 200,000 miles of track would be steel. By the turn of the century, steel rails accounted for 93 percent of the 258,000 miles of track that served as the nation's circulatory system.

Undeterred by the failure of the American Steeled Rail project, Thomas S. Blair continued working to answer the question that was confounding inventors and manufacturers across the iron and steel industry: How can steel be made more easily and economically? Of course "easily and economically" really meant "fast and cheap." In the US particularly, the development of the Bessemer process was shaped by the need to meet the railroads' insatiable appetite for steel, so quantity was the name of the game, not quality. Therefore, while the biggest iron and steel manufacturers scrambled to build their Bessemer works, Blair channeled his inventive energies into finding a way to make steel differently and potentially better—that is, with less waste, fewer costs, and of consistently good quality.

In addition to his patent for steel-headed rails, Blair was issued at least six other US patents and a handful of British patents for his processes and inventions, including one that described a design for a furnace that would convert lengths of "ordinary iron railroad-rails" into steel rails. Again, Blair's vision was on the mark, but the technology was not sound enough to gain traction in the industry. For the next few years, Blair experimented with manufacturing steel from "pig-bloom" and "pig-scrap," metals that were a combination of cast-iron and iron oxide, instead of wrought iron. In concept, these "crude metals" were cheaper than wrought iron and would produce a better result. Furthermore, the loose, porous texture of the pig-bloom and pig-scrap would melt faster, and the process would burn out more impurities than other processes could. Blair's method proposed to improve upon the recently patented Ellershausen process and included the use of an apparatus (also patented) that would reduce the manual labor involved in making the pig-bloom or pig-scrap used in the process.

Thomas Blair was on the cusp of a major breakthrough. In the late 1860s, inventors and metallurgists in Germany, France, and Great Britain were making crucial discoveries. Blair wanted to see it all for himself and learn from the brilliant minds in the industry, so he went to Europe. He had already applied for at least two British patents related to the steelmaking experiments he was conducting in the US, and in 1869 he became a member of the British Economic Association. In 1872, Blair joined the British Iron and Steel Institute, a group he believed "embod[ied] the latest and most advanced ideas in everything that relates to iron metallurgy."

During his years abroad, Blair took an interest in tidal power, which sought to harness energy generated by the movement of ocean tides. He visited sites in France to observe experimental tidal power stations but abandoned his studies when he concluded that there was no significant energy at work beneath the surface movement of the water.

Blair spent about three years in Europe, his thoughts and theories about steel smoldering all the while. When he returned to Pittsburgh, his brain was aflame with an idea that could revolutionize steelmaking. He'd identified the potential for "iron sponge" in the manufacture of refined iron and steel. Like the pig-scrap and pig-blooms he'd experimented with previously, iron sponge was a material that could be made at a lower cost than pig iron and would produce a better grade of steel. In May 1872, Blair was granted a patent for using iron sponge alone and in combination with wrought iron to make malleable iron and steel and was issued two additional patents that supported his iron sponge process. In the specifications for his patent for an improved version of iron sponge, Blair describes his product in detail:

The iron sponge which I manufacture is the product obtained by treating oxides of iron in contact with carbon at a suitable heat, and with practically-complete isolation from the atmosphere . . . After reduction, the [iron sponge] retains the general contour or shape of the ore or cinder from which it is derived, but somewhat expanded in bulk, and with very marked loss of weight. It has a very open or spongy texture; is readily sectile; is easily indented by the finger-nail; chews like lead between the teeth, and polishes quickly to a silvery luster.

The usefulness of iron sponge was only the first part of Thomas Blair's breakthrough in steelmaking. Blair had become deeply interested in the open-hearth process, a method of manufacturing steel developed mainly by Charles William Siemens (aka Karl Wilhelm Siemens), a British inventor and engineer of German birth. The open-hearth process and its associated Siemens regenerative gas furnace overcame some of the limitations of the Bessemer process and converter. The open-hearth process took much longer than a sudden, violent Bessemer blow, which created opportunities to test the steel at intervals and to adjust its properties to meet particular specifications. It was possible to use scrap metal in the open-hearth process, and the method could produce larger volumes of steel at a time than a Bessemer converter.

While the Cambria Iron Works and other manufacturers leveraged the Bessemer process to pump out steel rails for the ravenous railroads at a breakneck clip, Thomas Blair took his knowledge of iron sponge and open-hearth steelmaking and headed in the opposite direction, toward a scrupulous, cost-effective method of making steel that would produce a high-quality product. It was known as Blair's Direct Process, and it would become one of Thomas Shoenberger Blair's greatest triumphs and greatest disappointments.

The original Blair Homestead built by Captain Thomas Blair in the early 1780s still stands in Foot of Ten in Blair County. The building has seen many additions and renovations, but it remains a residential property. *Blair Strip Steel Company / Whitney Tressel, 2017*

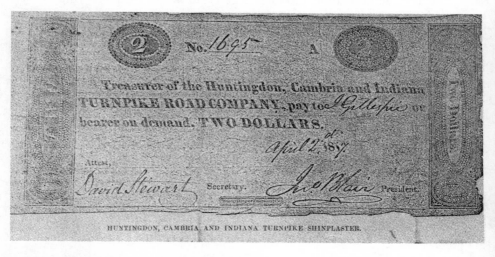

Led by president John Blair, the Huntingdon, Cambria and Indiana Turnpike Company issued "shinplasters" to help fund the construction of a turnpike road that would improve transportation across the Allegheny Ridge. This shinplaster was issued on April 2, 1817 and signed by John Blair. *From* Meet the Blair Family *by M.A. Miller*

During the first half of the 19th century, iron was made in charcoal-burning furnaces on plantations across the Pennsylvania countryside. The well-preserved remains of this furnace stack at Huntingdon Furnace in Huntingdon County is listed on the National Register of Historic Places. It was restored by the Newlin family in 2017. *Blair Strip Steel Company / Whitney Tressel, 2017*

Early ironmaster Dr. Peter Shoenberger was considered "The Iron King" of Pennsylvania. Andrew Carnegie was said to have remarked that Shoenberger was to iron what Carnegie himself was to steel. *From* The Iron King *by Calvin Hetrick*

The first page of a letter from Thomas Shoenberger Blair describing a railroad rail with "the wearing surface of steel & the body of iron." Blair formed The American Steeled Rail Company with Andrew Carnegie and Thomas Carnegie (Andrew's brother) around 1866. The venture would not be a success, but the Carnegies would go on to found the Edgar Thomson Steel Works, the most prolific all-steel rail mill in the country. *Blair Family*

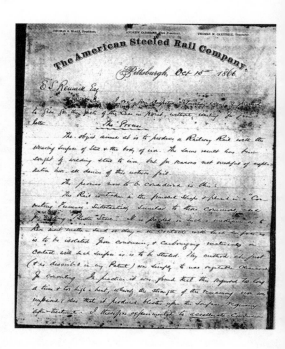

In 1847, iron manufacturer John H. Shoenberger built a town home at 425 Penn Avenue in Pittsburgh. The late Greek Revival house was considered one of the most luxurious residences in the downtown area. In the early 1880s, Shoenberger gave the building to the Pittsburgh Club, an exclusive social club for businessmen that had broken off from the famed Duquesne Club. *Library of Congress, Prints & Photographs Division, HABS PA,2-PITBU,9--1 / Louis Stevens, 1935*

An 1870 letter from Shoenberger & Blair & Co. to George Wilson Smith, secretary of corporate lawyer and 1876 Democratic candidate for president Samuel J. Tilden. Thomas Shoenberger Blair and his partners were known for their high-quality iron products, but by 1879, they would change course and begin making steel to compete with the likes of Carnegie Steel and Jones & Laughlin. *Shoenberger & Blair, New York Public Library Digital Collections, Manuscripts and Archives Division, The New York Public Library.*

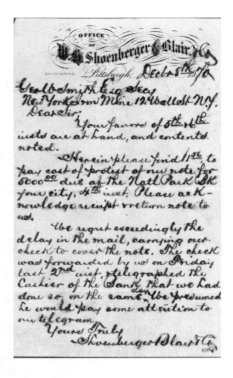

John and Margaret Shoenberger commissioned artist Jacob Eichholtz to paint portraits of several of their family members, including Florinda Cust Blair, sister of Margaret and mother of Thomas Shoenberger Blair. Titled *Mrs. Thomas Blair*, the portrait was painted in 1837. *Joan Dix Blair*

Portrait of Thomas Shoenberger Blair (ca. 1825–1899), iron and steel manufacturer, inventor, and philosopher

Around 1899, George D. Blair partnered with renowned cold-rolled steelmakers the Elliotts in New Castle, PA, to form Elliott-Blair Cold Roll Steel Co. This advertisement for the company ran in the *New Castle News* on July 28, 1922, not long before George Blair and his son, George, parted ways with the Elliott brothers to form the Blair Strip Steel Company. *Newspapers.com / New Castle Library*

George D. Blair (lower right), founder of the Blair Strip Steel Company, was among the most prominent businessmen in New Castle in the early years of the 20th century. *New Castle Library*

The charter forming the Blair Strip Steel Company was signed on December 31, 1923. *Blair Strip Steel Company*

A major fire at Blair Strip Steel was second only to the start of the World Series in the evening edition of the *New Castle News* on October 1, 1930. *Newspapers.com / New Castle Library*

Two men survey the damage caused by the fire that started in the main building at Blair Strip Steel on the morning of October 1, 1930.
Blair Strip Steel Company

George D. Blair, Jr. (sitting, center), his infant son Robert "Dike" Blair, and wife Hazel Slingluff Blair sit for a portrait with members of the Slingluff family and George's parents, George Blair, Sr. (back right) and Katherine Almeda Henderson Blair (standing, center) in September 1919. *Blair Family*

George D. Blair, Jr. on horseback, 1928. Like his father, George enjoyed recreational riding and was interested in trotting horses and harness racing. His son, Tom, would also have an affinity for horses and enjoy horse racing and handicapping as hobbies. *Blair Family*

Portrait of George D. Blair
Blair Strip Steel Company

Portrait of George D. Blair, Jr.
Blair Strip Steel Company

Tom Blair and Dike Blair as boys, ca.1929
Blair Family

Reba Blair and Dike Blair, ca.1943
Blair Family

THOMAS S. BLAIR, president Blair
Strip Steel Co.

A headshot accompanies the announcement in
The Iron Age magazine that Tom Blair was taking
over as president of Blair Strip Steel following
the death of his father. Tom was 27 years old.
from The Iron Age, *May 26, 1949*

• **Thomas S. Blair** has been elected
president of Blair Strip Steel Co.,
New Castle, Pa., succeeding his
father, George D. Blair, Jr., who
died. Prior to his new position,
Mr. Blair served as associated
editor of THE IRON AGE and had
previously been engaged in research on the Manhattan Project
at Columbia University in New
York and at Oak Ridge, Tenn.

BLAIR STRIP STEEL COMPANY
NEW CASTLE, PENNSYLVANIA

To All Employees:

We want to thank all of you − − whichever
way you voted − − for taking part in yesterday's election.

The Election gave all of us a chance to look
at the kind of setup we have. And we think it's good that it
did this.

The Election gave us a chance to explain things
about the Company which perhaps you didn't know or hadn't
thought about. And, at the same time, it brought out questions
which individuals may have had for a long time − − but which
they had hesitated to discuss.

We were very serious in our letters in saying
that it's a great asset to any Company for everyone involved
to be able to discuss things directly with each other. We have
such a setup. And we'll do our best to keep this direct and
close relationship intact. In return, we hope that you'll not
hesitate to come forward with questions and suggestions that
may develop.

All of us have a stake in the way things go in
the future. We'll all be better off by pulling together.

Cordially,

Thos. S. Blair

One of the letters Tom Blair wrote to his
employees amidst pressures to unionize in
1951. *Blair Strip Steel Company*

Portrait of Thomas S. Blair
Blair Strip Steel Company

The original "little white house" that served as the company's main office, circa late 1940s.
Blair Strip Steel Company

Blair Strip Steel commissioned the American painter John Rogers to capture steelmaking scenes at the Blair plant. This painting depicts men operating a rolling mill.

Men load coils of finished steel onto a truck in *Loading Platform* by John Rogers. *Blair Strip Steel Company*

Men remove steel from the annealing room in *Pulling a Heat - Rear Annealing Room* by John Rogers. *Blair Strip Steel Company*

President Jim Stillwagon accepts an award from Timken on behalf of Blair Strip Steel, ca.1990. *Blair Strip Steel Company*

(l to r) Foreman Emil Smolnik, Walter Makarevich, Gene Hardsock, and Dave Aiken pause for a photo in the machine shop at Blair Strip Steel in 1979. *Glenn Turner*

(l to r) Tom Stoops, Wayne Jordan, and Jim Hoagland work on the rolling mill known now as "Little Tom" in the late 1980s. A 2-stand, 4-high mill, "Little Tom" was named in honor of Tom Blair. *Blair Strip Steel Company*

(l to r) Glenn Turner, Larry Wimer, Jack Allen, and Ken Harris at the Blair main office, February 1987 *Blair Strip Steel Company*

Jack Allen and Tut Mills, 1985 *Glenn Turner*

Tom Blair and Jack Allen at the Blair main office in February 1987
Blair Strip Steel Company

(l to r) Tom Van Driel, John Avau, Bill Cody, Larry Wimer, Tom Blair, Dick Black, Glenn Turner, Ken Harris, and Bob Laird with president Jim Stillwagon at the Blair main office in the late 1990s *Blair Strip Steel Company*

Mill superintendent Glenn Turner (left) and president Austin Murphy (right) accept an award from GM on behalf of Blair, 1985. *Blair Strip Steel Company*

(l to r) Tom Van Driel, Jack Allen, and Bill Cody, at the Blair main office, February 1987 *Blair Strip Steel Company*

CHAPTER 4

MAKING *PROGRESS*: THE LIFE AND LEGACY OF THOMAS SHOENBERGER BLAIR

A lifetime seems in history's span
Short as a day, and yet a man
Invents and fashions things that last
Long after his brief breath has passed.
—Louise Shaw

As Thomas Shoenberger Blair knew well, many inventors and engineers had attempted to develop a direct process—a method for making steel directly from the ore instead of from pig iron—but all had failed. He himself had spent two decades trying to make the process work consistently, and with mixed results. The concept was relatively simple: The first step was to reduce the iron ore, and the second was to fuse it with enough carbon to create a malleable iron or steel. If the process were indeed that simple, Blair wondered, then why had so many brilliant inventors failed to make the process viable? What metallurgical or mechanical assumption was the stumbling block? What thing had been repeatedly overlooked?

By the early 1870s, Blair believed he had found the solution. He built his own steel works in Glenwood (today's Hazelwood neighborhood in Pittsburgh near the Glenwood Bridge) and in the spring of 1873 formed Blair Iron and Steel Company with Thomas Struthers and Morrison Foster. He hired a scholarly young engineer and fellow Harvard man Henry M. Howe away from his role as superintendent of a Bessemer operation at the very large, very promising Joliet Iron and Steel Company near Chicago to consult at Blair's Glenwood Works. Blair wanted to use a Siemens regenerative gas furnace in his open-hearth shop—one of the first open-hearth operations in the US— but he was denied a license; using his patented iron sponge was deemed a violation of the Siemens licensing agreement. Blair looked elsewhere for a gas furnace that would suit his needs. He found one close to home, using a model developed by H. Frank of Pittsburgh. In the final months of the year, while the iron industry and the US economy reeled from the Panic of 1873, a financial crisis that started a depression, Thomas Blair made steel, documented his methods, and prepared to present his direct process to the world.

In February 1874, Blair gave a talk at the New York meeting of the American Institute of Mining Engineers (AIME) titled, "The 'Direct Process' in Iron Manufacture." He recounted the history of difficulties other inventors had encountered with the process and praised the efforts of those who'd come close to making it work. Then, with a run of elegant rhetorical touches, Blair led his audience to the million-dollar question: If reducing ore directly is cheaper than using pig-iron, and melting the reduced ore is cheaper than puddling, and the result is a more valuable product, why weren't manufacturers employing these cost-cutting measures?

Blair was ready with an answer. "There has been a link missing," he proclaimed to his peers, "without it, all is naught. The missing link is true iron sponge." He went on to explain in detail the nuances of his iron sponge, its crucial role in the direct process for producing cast steel, and an analysis of the cost savings in fuel and raw materials. At the end of his lengthy remarks, before thanking his "associate and colaborer," Morrison Foster, Blair mentioned one final advantage of his direct process—a reason apart from his fellow manufacturers' profit margins. "I refer to the humanitarian view," he said.

> The word "puddling" finds no place in the direct process.
> No such exhausting, overtaxing labor is demanded in any
> of its operations, as it is the truly scientific method of iron
> metallurgy, so does it, in common with all true science, point
> to the ultimate reconcilement of capital and labor.

This nod, albeit brief, to the well-being of the workers who did the strenuous, highly dangerous job of "puddling"—melting iron and purifying it until it reached a pasty consistency and then using brute force to gather the decarburized metal into balls and pull them out of the furnace to be further refined—offered a glimpse into the profound concerns of Thomas

Blair's mind and soul. These concerns underpinned his way of being in the world, and he would revisit them with a lifetime of experience after his iron and steel days were over.

Upon closing his remarks, Blair invited questions about the quality of the ores he used and other details of his process. One attendee asked Blair how he treated workers who became nauseated from inhaling carbonic oxides released with the furnace's exhaust gases. "Ammonia (spirits of hartshorn), applied to the nostrils"—that is, smelling salts— was Blair's tried-and-true remedy.

On the whole, the audience was impressed. One attendee remarked, with a healthy sense of humor, "As a humanitarian, I am delighted, as a pig-metal manufacturer I am in the depths of despair. . . . All my beautiful plans for new furnaces must be stowed away with the inscription, 'What might have been if it hadn't been for Blair.'" The comment probably drew a rueful chuckle from the crowd, as many attendees may have had the same thought. "In behalf of the pig-iron makers of the United States," the commenter continued, "I appeal to Mr. Blair to follow the example of Dr. Siemens, to surround his process with such restrictions, and to charge such excessive royalties, that we may for this generation, at least, rather die by slow combustion than meet a violent and hasty death by carbonic oxide." Blair, showing his own playful side, reminded his colleague that he'd said "the old process will be *overgrown*, not *overthrown*."

There was hearty agreement from industry experts: Blair's idea was brilliant. Blair continued to refine his process at his Glenwood Works, and in June 1874, he applied for a US patent specifying "Improvement in the Manufacture of Steel by the Open-Hearth Process." The patent was approved in September of the same year.

That fall, renowned ironmaster and president of the British Iron and Steel Institute Mr. Isaac Lowthian Bell traveled to the United States to visit mines and put an eye on America's iron works. He spent most of his three-day stay in Pittsburgh at the Glenwood Works, observing Blair's Direct Process in action. Blair and company vice president Morrison Foster, who also served as superintendent of the mill, entertained Bell and his son and invited them to scrutinize every part of their operation. After the visit, Foster wrote:

Our books, showing the exact amount in pounds of every
component of each charge, and the resulting product in
pounds of every cast of steel made by us from the beginning,

were thrown open to him and were freely and fully inspected
. . . Every facility which any of [us] enjoyed for seeing or
knowing what was being done in and about every department
of the works was cheerfully given him, our object (aside from
showing deserved courtesy to so distinguished a stranger)
being to enable him to criticize our operations with full
knowledge of their details.

Bell's visit was a big break for Blair. Bell's reports about his experience
would be excellent publicity, especially abroad, and his approval could
do wonders for the process's credibility. And so, Blair and Foster were
likely shocked when they read Bell's remarks given to the British Iron
and Steel Institute the following spring. Bell expressed concern about the
susceptibility of iron sponge to oxidation, leading him to conclude that "the
direct process, as it is termed, has met with the most success at Landore,"
the steel works in Wales run by Siemens—not at Glenwood.

Bell went on to speculate about the amount of waste in Blair's process.
"So far as I was able to learn," he remarked, "two parts of pig iron and one
of sponge lost about 20 per cent in the furnace. Now, if it be true, as I have
heard stated, that a mixture of wrought iron and pig iron can be fused in an
open hearth with a loss of 6 per cent, it follows that a considerable portion of
the sponge used in Mr. Blair's process must be reoxidized." In concluding his
analysis of Blair's Direct Process, Bell softened his previous remarks with a bit
of equivocation. "The specimens of steel I had an opportunity of examining
indicate entire success, so far as a mere question of quality in the product is
concerned," he said. "I am far from wishing to be understood as expressing
an unfavourable opinion on the future commercial merits of the scheme."
He allowed that his "friend, Mr. T.S. Blair" had "made a notable step" in
advancing the technology, but in total, this was hardly a glowing review.

To Blair and Foster, Bell's remarks were, at best, a case of faulty
memory, and at worst, a deliberate betrayal. Hadn't Bell scoured their
production records? Hadn't Bell taken meticulous notes with the help of
his son? Nowhere did the documentation from the Glenwood Works show
the ratio of pig iron to sponge that Bell ultimately reported. Furthermore,
Bell had seen firsthand that the iron sponge did not float on the melted pig
when thrown into the furnace; it was kept from the surface by a layer of
slag, which prevented excessive oxidation. Indeed, as Morrison Foster later
argued, "This remarkable and interesting fact was noticed and commented
on with much pleasure by Mr. Bell at that time." Finally, Bell's comparison

of the Glenwood operation to the works at Landore was misapplied. Siemens and company were making steel suitable for rails, while Blair was attempting to make a higher-grade product for other applications.

Blair and Foster attempted to remedy the unexpected bad publicity immediately. Foster submitted letters to the editors of influential industry publications including *American Manufacturer* and *Scientific American*, addressing and refuting firmly yet respectfully (as was the gentlemanly thing to do) Bell's inaccurate claims. Blair again spoke at the meeting of the AIME, rebutting Bell's remarks about the amount of loss in his process while they were "still fresh in the minds of the American public." The meeting was attended by some of the most important players in the iron and steel industry, including Alexander Holley. Holley was an American engineer who had built six of the seven Bessemer works operating in the US between 1865 and the fall of 1872, including Andrew Carnegie's massive Edgar Thomson Works in Braddock, directly across the Monongahela from Blair's Glenwood Works.

A discussion followed Blair's talk, and Holley defended Blair's claims, stating that he had examined the records and found that Blair had not understated the amount of loss in his process. Holley acknowledged the question on the minds of many. If the Blair process were so effective, why had it not already been introduced to the steelmaking world? "The answer is—and it should be satisfactory," Holley said, "that Mr. Blair's only delay and embarrassment has been due to a bad open-hearth furnace—to a part of the plant entirely independent of his own patented and novel process and machinery." Holley explained how Blair had been barred from using a Siemens furnace at first, but then Holley himself convinced "Mr. Siemens" to let Blair buy a license for a furnace, which allowed Blair to "[have] uniform and sufficient heat" to produce "uniform steel." Henry Howe, another reputable voice in the industry and former consultant for Blair Iron and Steel, said he was "glad to be able to confirm Mr. Holley's statements in every particular." From his firsthand knowledge of the Glenwood operation, he vouched for Blair's difficulty stemming from the Frank furnace, not the iron sponge.

There was an additional back-and-forth between the Blair camp (Thomas Blair and Morrison Foster) and Sir Isaac Bell in letters to the editor of the *American Manufacturer*. To help vindicate the reputation of his process, Thomas Blair published a pamphlet with highlights from their correspondence and the proceedings from the AIME meeting titled *Mr. I. Lowthian Bell and the Blair Direct Process*, but the public relations damage was already done. It is difficult to know exactly why Bell's opinion of Blair's process was lukewarm at best when he had shown such enthusiasm during his visit. Perhaps the quaint process developed by a small-time American manufacturer hadn't impressed him much, and his encouraging words were merely a show of English good manners.

Or perhaps it was not politesse but politics. In Bell's view, the process might have been a threat to iron manufacturers like Bell himself. If Blair's process could do away with most of the pig iron or wrought iron required in steelmaking and the process became widely accepted, then surely the pig iron industry would suffer. It is also possible that Bell's man was Siemens, a fellow Brit and proven winner in the industry. If Bell were to openly endorse anyone in the open-hearth steelmaking game, it would be Siemens.

Though he'd come to Blair's defense at the AIME meeting, Henry Howe knew Blair's process had flaws. In his book *The Metallurgy of Steel* published fifteen years later, Howe devoted several pages to Blair's Direct Process and gave his analysis of why it never caught on. Firstly, he wrote, the process was very slow, and though Blair and Foster claimed that adding a certain amount of lime to the charge accelerated the process, Howe wasn't convinced. Furthermore, the iron sponge was said to take on carbon in the presence of carbonic acid as it cooled, but in Howe's testing of the process, he was not able to replicate the same result. Just as Bell had done in his remarks and letters, Howe took up the issue of how to calculate loss. In his opinion, it came down to how well an open-hearth furnace was managed, "and as I know well"—because he had been employed at the Glenwood Works—"this particular open-hearth furnace (Franks) was not well managed." Notably, he did not include loss calculations after Blair switched to a better furnace (a Siemens), probably because Howe had left Glenwood by then for a career in metallurgy outside steel mills.

Howe's final word on the subject suggests that it wasn't unsound ideas that sank Blair's Direct Process but a combination of errors in practice (the initial faulty furnace) and some unidentified bad luck. "I have attributed the failure of the process less to its being inapplicable to existing conditions," he wrote, "than to injudicious management, in carrying out avoidable experiments (as if unavoidable ones were not burdensome enough), and to certain misfortunes for which the management seemed in no way to blame."

In the end, perhaps Blair's Direct Process was simply not quite ready for a larger stage, and unlike Henry Bessemer, he didn't have the marketing clout to insist it was. There was brilliance in Thomas S. Blair's concept, but there were still kinks to work out when he introduced it to his steelmaking colleagues. As Bessemer remarked in his autobiography, "An invention must be nursed and tended as a mother nurses her baby, or it inevitably perishes." No doubt Blair had nurtured his invention, but unfortunately, the flaws of his process were brought to light before he could develop it further.

The mid-1870s were a significant moment in the history of the American iron and steel industry. As scholar John N. Ingham described it, "a relatively stable and prosperous iron industry was on the brink of a great Bessemer steel revolution." In 1874, the industry was comprised of numerous small-sized to medium-sized producers, and they were not yet making much steel. Over the next twenty-five years, the landscape would change profoundly. Many small firms gave way to a few massive corporations who could use the Bessemer process to pump out endless quantities of commodity steel.

In late summer 1875, the Edgar Thomson Works, built by Thomas Blair's old partner, Andrew Carnegie, and named to honor—and perhaps flatter—Carnegie's former boss and Pennsylvania Railroad man, J. Edgar Thomson, began operations as the first Bessemer mill in Pittsburgh and the largest steel mill in the world. Its purpose was to make large volumes of steel rails for the railroads as rapidly as possible. The behemoth Edgar Thomson Works would become the symbol of the "large, integrated corporations" of the future.

But not every producer fell victim to the new way of "big" steel. In his book *Making Iron and Steel: Independent Mills in Pittsburgh, 1820–1920*, Ingham argues against the traditional narrative that smaller iron- and steelmakers were inevitably gobbled up by Carnegie's mills and other large companies. Instead, he claims "a majority of older Pittsburgh iron and steel men" decided to specialize and seek new markets so as not to have to compete with the larger producers. It is unknown whether Thomas Shoenberger Blair was among those experienced producers who chose to stay small and specialized. When Carnegie's Thomson Works began operations across the river, Blair's Glenwood Works was already making high-quality grades of steel for applications other than rails. However, Blair Iron and Steel had been hurt by production inconsistencies and bad publicity, and the company was faltering. In 1876, early investors in the company, including up-and-coming American banker John Pierpont "J.P." Morgan, requested and eventually sued for a refund of the capital stock they had purchased in Blair Iron and Steel when the company was founded three years earlier. The end of the company, as well as the end of steelmaking by Blair's patented process, began then or soon after.

Even though his direct process did not revolutionize steelmaking and Blair Iron and Steel Company was not a long-term success, manufacturing was ultimately a lucrative career for Thomas Blair. Throughout his experimentation with the direct process, he remained in business with the Shoenbergers. In the early 1860s, while Blair was managing the operations of their nail rolling mill, he became a partner in the firm newly renamed Shoenberger & Co. By the late 1860s, Shoenberger & Co. was making horseshoes of superior quality—and making a fortune on them—thanks to the Ellershausen process. In 1868, Blair, the Shoenberger brothers, and other investors formed Shoenberger, Blair, & Company to finance and operate a pair of blast furnaces that each towered 62 feet high and together at capacity produced 48,000 tons of iron a year.

As competitors Carnegie Steel and Jones & Laughlin began to outpace them in their traditional markets, Shoenberger, Blair, and Company changed course. In 1879–81, with Thomas Blair as plant manager, they installed a twelve-ton Siemens-Martin open-hearth furnace that could make specialty products like sheet steel, plate steel, and steel boiler plate. They also added two six-ton Bessemer converters in 1886. Though these changes helped, the Shoenbergers' reign in the iron and steel industry was coming to an end. Following the deaths of John H. Shoenberger in 1889 and two other key members of the family in the early 1890s, the company was reorganized. The new owners, who were relatives of the Shoenbergers by marriage, were unable to navigate the downturn in the economy. In 1899, they sold the Juniata Iron Works to American Steel Wire, an industry power player that would become one of the foundational pieces of the United States Steel Corporation (aka US Steel) in 1901.

———

As serious an intellectual, scientist, and businessman as Thomas Shoenberger Blair was, he was also thoroughly humane. "Personally, Mr. Blair was a delightful companion," wrote one of his contemporaries in tribute to him. "He was an American gentleman of the old school . . . He was singularly handsome though not notably of large build . . . as much at home in a drawing room as in an office or his own study . . . His keen wit and gentle humor were sources of constant merriment to his family and friends."

Family was an elemental force in Thomas Shoenberger Blair's universe. First, there was the early loss of his father, followed by the good fortune of moving into the Shoenberger household. Within a few years of returning to Pittsburgh after his year at Harvard, Thomas started his own family. In 1847, he married Virginia Dike of Steubenville, Ohio, whose ancestors were among the earliest settlers of the Plymouth colony and also included American writer Nathaniel Hawthorne. Virginia Dike's great-grandfather, George Woods, a surveyor, is credited with dividing into lots "the Town of Pittsburgh" in 1784.

In 1848, Thomas and Virginia Blair had their first son. They named him John Shoenberger Blair, to honor the man who'd become a second father to Thomas. It was also a gesture of deference to John and Margaret Shoenberger as a couple, for they were unable to have children of their own. In March 1851, while the Blairs were expecting their second child, young John died; he was just two years old. A month later, George Dike Blair was born. He was likely named for Virginia's brother, grandfather, and great-grandfather. The Blairs had a daughter, Anna Dike Blair, in 1859 and a son, Thomas S. Blair, Jr., in 1863.

The Blair family lived in Glenwood, not far from the eventual site of the Blair Iron and Steel Company's Glenwood Works. Prior to the Civil War, Glenwood had been a rural escape for the elite families of Pittsburgh. With the sprawl of the iron and steel industry it became one of the self-contained manufacturing towns along the Monongahela, complete with mills, row houses, churches, taverns, and railroad lines that traced the curve of the river. The Blairs lived on the hill above Second Avenue, on land Virginia Dike Blair had inherited from her Woods relatives. Their large, three-story house was surrounded by open, manicured grounds, a garden, and an orchard, which made it more like a country estate than a home in the city. Many streets in the neighborhood were named for families and individuals connected with the Blairs, including Blair, Dyke (Dike), Cust, Elizabeth, Lytle, and Johnston.

Over the course of just a few weeks late in the summer of 1878, Thomas Blair lost the three most important women in his life. On August 9, his wife, Virginia, died at the age of fifty and was laid to rest in Union Cemetery in her hometown of Steubenville. On August 30, Margaret Cust Shoenberger, Thomas's beloved aunt, died of breast cancer at the age of sixty-eight. "In loving memory" of his wife, John Shoenberger endowed St. Margaret Memorial Hospital, bequeathing $800,000 (about $20.5 million in 2020) and three acres of land on the Shoenberger family summer estate in the Lawrenceville neighborhood. St. Margaret's Hospital was dedicated in 1898 and operated on its original site until 1980, when it was moved across the river to provide health care in an underserved area. The hospital operates today as UPMC St. Margaret.

Four days after Margaret Shoenberger died, Florinda Cust Blair, sister of Margaret and mother of Thomas, died at the age of seventy-eight. Florinda was laid to rest in Allegheny Cemetery beside Thomas and Virginia's young son, John. The boy's namesake, John Shoenberger, had helped found the cemetery and donated land for the cemetery's expansion. A monument to the Shoenberger family still stands in Allegheny Cemetery today.

Florinda Cust Blair would live on in her son's memory as she was when he was just a boy, thanks to a beautifully rendered portrait by the American artist Jacob Eichholtz. In 1834, when Thomas was eight or nine, Eichholtz was commissioned to paint five heads for the Shoenberger family, including portraits of Dr. Peter and Mrs. Shoenberger; their daughter, Anna Maria; Mary Cust, the mother of Margaret Cust Shoenberger and Florinda Cust Blair; and Florinda herself. These might have been a gift from John and Margaret Shoenberger, as their portraits were not painted at the time.

In her portrait, "Mrs. Thomas Blair" is portrayed as an elegant gentlewoman. Her complexion appears fair and alabaster-smooth, though she was in her mid-thirties when Eichholtz painted her likeness. She is "seated, facing right, hands folded in lap holding a glove; brown hair, parted in center, pinned high in back with curls at side, brown eyes . . . black silk dress with off-shoulder low neck, full sleeves, a fur over shoulders; red chair back showing to left, column in left background, landscape in distance with mountains and a lake and a setting sun near horizon." Though the background was not intended to be a true representation of the place where his subject actually sat for the portrait, Eichholtz likely began his painting at Dr. Shoenberger's Rebecca Furnace property in Huntingdon County, where the families had retreated after a cholera scare in Pittsburgh, and perhaps was inspired by the Allegheny Ridge. The portrait of Florinda Cust Blair remains in the Blair family today.

For Thomas Shoenberger Blair, losing his wife, his mother, and his beloved aunt in startling succession must have been a sobering reminder about the unpredictable and finite nature of life. The iron manufacturer wanted to do more with however much time he had left, and so in 1883, Blair sold his interest in Shoenberger, Blair, & Company. In 1884 he retired from the iron and steel business altogether. He was not yet sixty years old.

Though his aspirations for steelmaking had cooled, Blair's brilliant mind and his will to examine and inquire burned white-hot. He returned again to the earnest study of philosophy and political economy, which had captured his interest when he was a young scholar at Harvard. Blair read, thought, and wrote deeply about the concept of "human progress"—how humankind could evolve toward greater prosperity and well-being for all. He concluded that philosophers like Auguste Comte and John Stuart Mill, both of whom he studied seriously, were taking a misguided approach to achieving human progress. Abstract reasoning wasn't the answer. Empirical evidence, the kind collected and analyzed by scientists and businessmen, was.

In 1896, Blair published a book titled *Human Progress: What Can Man Do to Further It?* His self-described "little treatise" totals 573 pages, with the introduction alone topping one hundred pages. The central tenet of the book is that human progress is encouraged by adopting national economic and governmental policies based on "an enlightened self-interest." According to Blair's "Law of the Evolution of Human Wants," humans are by nature self-seeking, a condition that should not necessarily pit humans against one another. On the contrary, when humans can satisfy basic wants, higher-order desires will replace them, including the desire to behave morally and altruistically. And so, if the progression of wants is permitted and encouraged, humankind, too, can progress.

The author identified as "T.S. Blair" modestly disclaimed his book as "nothing more than a connected series of suggestions, tentative and conjectural," but some critics were impressed with his book and thought it was a worthy addition to the ongoing conversation about the state of humanity. One critic noted how different Blair's perspective on consumption was from other economic theories of the time. Instead of defining consumption as the destruction of wealth and therefore an "evil," Blair saw consumption as the conversion of wealth into well-being—a positive, constructive economic activity. Wrote the critic about Blair's fresh perspective, "[It] throws an absolutely new light upon the whole field, and transforms the 'dismal science' of economics, with what Mr. Blair calls its gospels of Helplessness, Hopelessness and Hate, into a science of optimism, progress and hope." Though most political economists and philosophers would have recognized the author's knowledge of business, few would have guessed that T.S. Blair was a Pittsburgh ironmaster, as comfortable on the floor of a rolling mill as he was in the text of a dense philosophical treatise.

Thomas Shoenberger Blair lived to see his magnum opus published, but his health was waning. In the autumn of 1898, he contracted a case of bronchitis that became too severe for his system to overcome. He died at the home of his daughter and son-in-law in Pittsburgh at the age of seventy-three. His remains were taken to Steubenville and buried beside Virginia's.

Thomas Shoenberger Blair was not content to live as just a manufacturer, businessman, inventor, or philosopher. Instead, he followed each strand of his curiosity, picking up knowledge and experience and leaving behind things insightful, original, and useful. He dwelled in the cerebral realm of theory and on the mill floor of practice, a thinker and a maker until the end.

CHAPTER 5

TRAVELING NEW ROADS: GEORGE D. BLAIR AND THE BIRTH OF BLAIR STRIP STEEL

We just developed an idea. The nucleus of a business may be an idea. That is, an inventor or a thoughtful workman works out a new and better way to serve some established human need; the idea commends itself, and people want to avail themselves of it.

—Henry Ford,
American industrialist and business magnate (1863–1947)

George Dike Blair was born under the sooty skies of Pittsburgh in 1851, when the Iron City was busily earning its name. His father, Thomas Shoenberger Blair, a bright young ironmaster, was in the thick of it, managing operations for the Shoenbergers and developing methods for making cast steel. Young George attended private school first in Pittsburgh and then at St. Paul's School for boys in Concord, New Hampshire, nestled among ponds and woods. Unlike in Pittsburgh, a boy had room to breathe and wander at St. Paul's; he could go fishing after the day's lessons were done. The place cultivated in George a love for life in the country. In some ways, it felt more like home than his family's house in the city.

George continued his education in earnest at the University of Heidelberg in Germany. He learned the German language and studied the country's manufacturing methods, his German education only enhancing his naturally analytical disposition. George's siblings Anna and Thomas, younger by eight and twelve years, also attended schools in Germany while their father sharpened his scientific and metallurgical knowledge in the iron and steel industry across Europe. George knew he was destined to join the family iron and steel business, but his first stop was not Pittsburgh. It was Chicago.

In 1872, George Blair became the secretary and treasurer of the Excelsior Pressed Brick Manufacturing Company, an outfit that had begun to mass produce bricks from a rich clay deposit about eighteen miles outside Chicago. With its Excelsior Pressed Brick Machine, the company could produce quality bricks faster and in much larger quantities than the manual brick-makers in the city—up to 140,000 bricks per day. It was a good time to be in the brick business. The Great Chicago Fire had incinerated the city's business district a year earlier, and reconstruction was focused on the use of fireproof building materials like brick and terra cotta clay.

After two years with the brick manufacturer, George resigned and returned to Pittsburgh to manage the Glenwood Works of his father's Blair Iron and Steel Company. His time there was equally brief. When the company folded, George became the manager of the Shoenbergers' Huntingdon Furnace property in rural Huntingdon County. The furnace itself was no longer in blast—charcoal had given way to mineral fuels in ironmaking—but the property included several buildings and a large tract of productive farmland, all of which George oversaw.

In this way, George Blair had found a way to get back to the country life that suited him so well. There he met Almeda Henderson, a young woman born and raised in Huntingdon County. The couple married in 1880 and had three children. Virginia Dike Blair, who was named for George's mother, was born in 1881. John Cust Blair was born in 1883 and George Dike Blair, Jr., in 1887.

In April 1891, the Blairs left Huntingdon Furnace and moved to nearby Tyrone, a growing borough that by the end of the nineteenth century was "the busiest stop on the Pennsylvania Railroad between Philadelphia and Pittsburgh." In 1896, George became the general manager and treasurer of the Iron City Fire Brick Company headquartered in Philipsburg. The newly formed company bought the Sandy Ridge Brick Works, which had been in operation for thirty years. The quantity and quality of the clay in the Sandy Ridge area made the Works one of the most productive brickyards in the country. Firebrick was an increasingly valuable product at the time, as iron and steel manufacturers were using it to line their furnaces. Firebrick was made to withstand very high temperatures and contact with white-hot metal, but it also supported the chemistry of the basic open-hearth process.

In addition to its plant at Sandy Ridge, Iron City Fire Brick Company operated a plant in Pittsburgh. Given his Pittsburgh connections and experience in the iron and steel industry, George Blair was an ideal candidate for managing the business in the city. He and his family moved to a grand house on Clyde Street in the East End among Pittsburgh's aristocratic class.

On January 22, 1898, while George was away on business and the family was having supper downstairs in the dining room, the Blairs were robbed. Allegedly, the burglars entered through an upstairs window and took between $600 and $1,000 in precious gems and jewelry— the equivalent of $18,000 and $31,000 in 2020. The daily newspapers described a series of similar burglaries in the area and how unusual they were. The *Pittsburgh Commercial Gazette* (future *Post-Gazette*) noted how the neighborhood was "one of the last places in the city the light-fingered gents would be suspected of visiting," given how close to the street the homes sat and the "electric lights flashing all about." No doubt the Blairs were rattled, too, especially since the man of the house was away when their safety and privacy were violated.

If George Blair hadn't been fond of city life or the trappings of high society to begin with, the burglary certainly didn't help. By the end of 1898, he had sold his interests in Iron City Fire Brick and moved his family sixty miles northwest to New Castle, Pennsylvania.

In 1898, New Castle was not as small as the borough of Tyrone, nor as rural as Huntingdon Furnace in Franklin Township, but it wasn't Pittsburgh, either. By the turn of the century, there were more than 300,000 people living in Pittsburgh, and it was the eleventh largest city in the United States. In comparison, the population of New Castle in 1890 was 11,600. But it was growing. In ten years' time, the population more than doubled, and by 1910 it had reached 38,280 people—more than three times the recorded population in 1890.

When the Blairs arrived in 1898, New Castle was already a manufacturing center and was rapidly becoming the tin plate capital of the world. The increase in the city's population from 1890 to 1910 was due in large part to the influx of immigrants from Britain, Finland, Hungary, Italy, Poland, Slovakia, Sweden, and Greater Syria, an area that encompassed present-day Syria, Israel, Jordan, and Lebanon. Most of the families came to "little Pittsburgh" seeking jobs in the mills.

The Blairs' move to New Castle also marked a new business venture for George. As early as 1897, while still affiliated with Iron City Fire Brick and living in Pittsburgh, he became involved with Elliott-Washington Steel, a New Castle company that produced cold-rolled strip steel. Cold rolling was still a relatively rare process in the landscape of American steelmaking in the late nineteenth century, but it was catching on. Manufacturers found that by passing steel through horizontal rolls at relatively low temperatures to reduce its thickness, they could produce steel with superior properties.

Brothers and native Englishmen Noah W. Elliott and George M. Elliott were considered among the best cold-rolled steelmakers in the United States. Noah Elliott started making steel at age sixteen and worked for several years in the rolling mill at Crescent Steel, a prominent crucible steelmaker in Pittsburgh. He became foreman at Singer, Nimick & Company and then was hired by Spaulding & Jenkins to establish a cold-rolled mill for the company in Jersey City, New Jersey. George joined Noah out east, and the two spent the next six years honing their cold rolling expertise. In 1891 the brothers returned to Pennsylvania and formed Elliott Bros. Steel Company in New Castle.

A few years into the venture, another brother, Thomas C. Elliott, joined Noah and George. When the operation needed additional funding in 1894, W.L. Washington—purported descendent of President George Washington—partnered with the brothers to create the Elliott-Washington Steel Company. Washington was president and general manager, Noah Elliott served as general superintendent, George Elliott led the rolling department, and Thomas Elliott took charge of annealing. The mill doubled in size during Washington's involvement.

In the spring of 1898, George Blair bought Washington's share of the firm, and it was renamed Elliott-Blair Cold Roll Steel Company. Blair replaced Washington as president and general manager, while the Elliott brothers continued to orchestrate the operations of the mill that sat at the corner of Taylor and Mercer Streets. Elliott-Blair manufactured light-gauge precision steels for the most steel-intensive equipment of the day, including sewing machines, typewriters, cash registers, adding machines, and bicycle parts. By 1908, the mill employed 100 men and was producing 7,000 tons of steel annually. Noah Elliott and George Blair were among the most prominent businessmen in New Castle.

In addition to his professional successes, George Blair enjoyed a gratifying private life in New Castle. Though it wasn't important to the Blairs to hobnob among the moneyed and socially prominent, they were well regarded in the community and lived comfortably in the North Hill neighborhood. The greater Lawrence County countryside just beyond the city allowed George Blair to engage with nature and the outdoors, a pastime that remained essential to him. He was the first president of the New Castle Golf Club when it was a nine-hole course on Vine Street in east New Castle. In 1922, he was one of the investors when the club moved north and expanded into the New Castle Field Club, which included an 18-hole golf course designed by A.W. Tillinghast. George Blair also owned horses for recreational riding and was interested in trotting horses and harness racing.

The 1910s remained a lucrative time for steelmakers in part because of the Great War in Europe. The United States' involvement spurred the production of steel nationwide. Mills churned out steel for helmets, boot shanks, knives, bayonets, bullet casings, and grenades. When the war ended in 1918, the demand for light-gauge steel dropped. Manufacturers were left with plenty of capacity for making the steel but no one to buy it. To further complicate matters, the US economy entered a brief but significant recession immediately following the war. With the end of wartime production and the return of the troops, there were more laborers than available jobs, which made for high unemployment. And then, before the country had fully shifted back to a peacetime economy, the Depression of 1920–21 descended. It began in January 1920—just ten months after the post–World War I recession—and showed the sharpest drop in wholesale prices since the American Revolution. The year 1920 would see the largest annual deflation in the history of the US.

The decrease in demand for light-gauge precision steel coupled with the economic depression forced Noah Elliott and George Blair to reassess their business strategy. Blair felt strongly that moving into heavy-gauge steel was essential for the long-term viability of Elliott-Blair. Early in his career, he had witnessed how the savviest of Pittsburgh's small, independent iron- and steelmakers made the decision to change course when Bessemer steelmaking and large, integrated works changed the marketplace. Instead of fighting for a spot doing what everyone else was trying to do at near-impossible volumes, they charted a new course and specialized.

But Elliott disagreed. Perhaps he thought Elliott-Blair could still compete for a share of the shrinking market. Perhaps he thought sticking with what the company already knew how to make was the key to riding out the tough economic times. After all, they had made a reputable name for themselves producing precision light-gauge cold-rolled steel, so going in a new direction may have seemed far too risky.

There also may have been a personal side to the partners' difference of opinion. Company lore suggests that Noah Elliott and George Blair were not particularly fond of each other. Though they must have existed together civilly enough to keep their business profitable for more than two decades, Elliott and Blair wanted as little to do with each other as possible.

As the story goes, the two had desks at opposite ends of the company office, and instead of communicating directly, each man would dictate a message to his secretary, who would then deliver the message to the other man's secretary, who would relay the message to her employer—despite the men working within sight of each other.

One can only speculate whether the relationship between Elliott and Blair truly was sour. If there is some kernel of truth in this story, then the men probably shed very few tears when George D. Blair, Sr., and his son, George D. Blair, Jr., who was also a manager in the company, sold their shares to members of the Elliott family and resigned from the board of directors in early 1923.

The Blairs decided to put their money on a horse their old partners thought was a longshot but they believed could really run. The horse was heavy-gauge strip steel, which the rising automobile industry would need for its parts—if it continued to grow. By late 1923, the Blairs and their financial partner, the Honorable J. Norman Martin, a retired judge in New Castle, had organized and funded the new company. On December 31, 1923, the state charter was signed, officially incorporating the Blair Strip Steel Company, manufacturer of cold-rolled precision products in thicknesses the nation hadn't yet seen.

The story that ran in the *New Castle News* in late November 1923 expressed unequivocal confidence in the Blairs' new venture. "There is every indication that the new concern will be a success from the outset," it read. Certainly neither George Blair, Sr., nor George Blair, Jr., could guarantee the success of their new company. They were, after all, creating a business almost solely dependent on the automobile industry, itself still relatively new and uncertain. The move must have felt like a risky bet.

It wasn't a blind bet, however. The Blairs had kept a keen eye on the rising popularity of automobiles and one in particular—Henry Ford's Model T. "I will build a motor car for the great multitude," Ford had said around the time he founded the Ford Motor Company in 1903:

> It will be large enough for the family but small enough for
> the individual to run and care for. It will be constructed
> of the best materials, by the best men to be hired, after the
> simplest designs that modern engineering can devise. But it
> will be so low in price that no man making a good salary will
> be unable to own one—and enjoy with his family the blessing
> of hours of pleasure in God's great open spaces.

The Model T, produced from 1908 to 1927, would fulfill Henry Ford's vision. Following the Great War and the postwar economic depression, sales of the Model T surged. The US middle class was expanding rapidly, and the infrastructure to support the new automotive culture—improved roads and bridges, gasoline stations, and service garages—was underway.

Ford priced his Model T such that middle-class families in urban and rural America could actually imagine buying an automobile, which previously had been considered a luxury contraption for the very rich. In October 1909, the base price of the Model T was set at $950 and over time would drop below $300. But, as historian Douglas Brinkley points out, "The appeal of Ford's 'car for the great multitude' lay not merely in its dramatically low cost but in its durability, ease of driving and simplicity to maintain. Model Ts were practical cars with which people could improve their lives and expand their horizons."

The Ford Motor Company sold more than 15 million "Tin Lizzies" between 1908 and 1927. In 1914 alone, it produced and sold more cars than the combined total sold throughout the rest of the world. By the early 1920s, as the Blairs were parting ways with the Elliotts, the Model T accounted for a staggering two-thirds of all vehicles on US roads. If the Model T's popularity was an accurate indicator, then an increasing demand for parts for the "horseless carriage" was looking like a smart wager.

By the end of January 1924, the new Blair Strip Steel Company had purchased the site for their operation and was poised to begin construction. The plant was situated on the east side of New Castle, between Butler Avenue, the railroad tracks of the Buffalo, Rochester, and Pittsburgh Railway, and steelmaker Castle Foundry. There was an air of local pride and optimism around the new steel outfit. "The Blair Strip Steel company is directly a New Castle corporation," wrote the *New Castle News* on January 28, 1924. "The men controlling it are New Castle men, the building will be erected by a New Castle firm, and the men who will be employed in the plant will be New Castle men." Indeed, Blair had hired the New Castle firm Smith & Bauman to build the plant. The brick and glass main building housed both the mill and the offices of the company, and side buildings held the pickling equipment. The mill ran on electric power provided by the New Castle Electric Company.

The "New Castle men" were, of course, founding partners George Blair, Sr., George Blair, Jr., and J. Norman Martin, as well as Thurman C. Post and George T. Weingartner. Together the group formed the company's first board of directors, electing Mr. Blair, Sr., president, Mr. Blair, Jr., vice president and treasurer, and Mr. Post secretary.

After waiting out inclement weather, construction on the Blair plant began in earnest in April 1924, and by September of the same year, the company was making steel. Blair's first customers included not only Ford but also Chevrolet, Chrysler, Dodge, Hudson, Oakland, Packard, and General Motors.

In very little time, Blair Strip Steel became a known entity in the industry. It helped that the US economy was entering a period of rapid growth and prosperity in manufacturing. During the "Roaring Twenties," US steelmakers produced 40 percent of the world's iron and steel. Thanks also to the booming auto industry, demand for Blair's heavy-gauge steel continued to increase. Before the plant was even three years old, plans for a 12,500-square-foot addition were underway. In the summer of 1927, it seemed the addition would be up and operational in no time at all and Blair would continue its climb.

The following spring, George Blair, Sr., became suddenly and gravely ill. He died on April 30, 1928—one day after his seventy-seventh birthday. His death was a blow to his family, friends, and colleagues. He had been well regarded among his business associates in Pittsburgh and central Pennsylvania, but in New Castle he was irreplaceable. For the thirty years he lived in Lawrence County, Mr. Blair was a champion not just for his business but also for industry throughout the area. He held firm the belief that the community would prosper if industry thrived. He had become a leader across business sectors, serving as director of the First National Bank of Lawrence County, the Union Trust Company of New Castle, Shenango Valley Hospital, and the Jameson Memorial Hospital Association. He served as a vestryman for Trinity Episcopal Church and during World War I supported the work of the Red Cross.

George D. Blair was the sort of civically engaged person whose distinguished presence and sound wisdom created an aura of benevolent invincibility and, above all else, gentlemanly poise. In a formal resolution, the board of directors of the First National Bank of Lawrence County honored George Blair, expressing profound respect and esteem for their colleague:

In his departure hence the Board of Directors has lost a wise
and faithful counselor, and the community an active and
substantial citizen. For such as he was, we mourn not, for his
life, well rounded out in the affairs that tend to make men more
successful citizens, remains with us an example to be drawn on
day by day in the affairs of business, life and manhood.

In the coming years and decades, George D. Blair's example would guide the strip mill on Butler Avenue, in times of prosperity and in times of hardship.

CHAPTER 6

HARD TIMES AND WARTIME: BLAIR STRIP STEEL COMES OF AGE

Sooner or later a crash is coming, and it may be terrific.
—Roger Babson, American entrepreneur
and business theorist (1875–1967)

Before he got into steel, George Dike Blair, Jr.—"Dike," as he was called to distinguish him from his father, George—was involved in the other big industry of the day: the railroad. Upon graduating from Cornell University in 1911, Dike began work as a traffic agent on the Union Line, a freight carrier in the sprawling Pennsylvania Railroad (PRR) system. His new job was based in South Bend, Indiana, a city that was an important industrial center at the time and home to several successful manufacturers, including the Studebaker Automobile Company.

It was likely that Dike had gotten the job with help from his brother-in-law, Henry Worth Thornton, a popular and successful manager with the PRR. Thornton was a strapping, All-American type, tall and broad with blue eyes and a gamely cleft chin. He'd secured the title of class president after one year at the University of Pennsylvania and became a star center and guard on the football squad. After graduating, Thornton coached football at Vanderbilt for a year, losing one game and winning seven, and then began his career as a draftsman for the PRR. He was promoted several times in the Pittsburgh office until he was made superintendent of the Erie & Ashtabula Division. He moved to the division headquarters in New Castle and lived on Highland Avenue, enjoying life as a young, eligible bachelor who'd risen quickly in his chosen profession.

As expected of a man of his standing, Thornton courted Virginia Dike Blair, daughter of George D. Blair (Sr.), one of the most successful businessmen in New Castle, and married her in 1901. The couple had two children, a boy and a girl, and appeared to be a thoroughly modern American family of the new upper crust.

In 1912, Thornton was promoted to General Superintendent of the Long Island Railroad, which had become another project of the mighty PRR. Thornton remained in that position until 1914 when London came calling. In the words of the chairman of the Great Eastern Railway of England, "We are unable to obtain in all England a general manager to cope with this, the most congested railway terminum in all of Christendom." Thornton seemed like just the man who could untangle the impossible logistical knot. He had a knack for organizing and inventing railroad procedures, and he also knew how to handle people, earning the respect of management and workers alike.

The opportunity abroad was good timing for Thornton. The onset of the War allowed him to further prove himself as a premier railroad man and an indispensable asset to a country in crisis. Other manufacturers and engineers from the Pittsburgh area were also recruited to help with transportation logistics for the Allied troops. One newspaper reporter from Pittsburgh wrote a story about the "wartime 'Pittsburgh Colony in London,'" which painted a rosy picture of American businessmen and their families enjoying picnics on the Thames and leisurely weekends at country estates, untouched and unbothered by the chaos and destruction of war.

For his wartime efforts, Thornton was knighted in 1919 and commissioned as Inspector General of Transportation. In 1922, Sir Henry Thornton left England to become President of the Canadian National Railway (CNR). During his ten-year career with the CNR, he reorganized and modernized the system and made many improvements to passenger travel. He also directed investment in the towns and cities along the railway routes, which helped them become appealing destinations instead of pass-throughs between larger tourist hubs.

While he spent liberally on the railway, Thornton also lived lavishly—and perhaps recklessly. In July 1926, Lady Virginia Blair Thornton divorced her husband "on grounds of indignities and continuous incompatibility." Not long after, Henry Thornton married the daughter of a prominent lawyer and commissioner in Nassau County, New York. Following the 1932 elections in Canada, the Conservative Party became the governing party and having long disapproved of his spending forced Thornton out of his position with the CNR. Though he had built an impressive career as a railroad man, Thornton died in disgrace less than a year after his resignation.

Despite Thornton's personal indiscretions, his presence in Dike Blair's life produced a good career opportunity for the young man—and a happier love story. While working on the Union Line, Dike met Hazel Elizabeth Slingluff, a young society woman from Canal Dover, Ohio. They were married in Hazel's hometown in June 1913 and returned to South Bend after "an extended trip East," which probably included a trip to visit the Blairs in New Castle. In 1916, Dike resigned from the PRR to work for Thornton in England. After the war, Dike and Hazel Blair returned to the United States and settled in New Castle, where Dike became a manager at Elliott-Blair Steel. On April 9, 1919, Robert Dike Blair was born to Mr. and Mrs. George Blair, Jr. They called him "Dike."

It was a good life. The families lived just around the corner from each other: George Sr. and Almeda on Leasure Avenue and George Jr., Hazel, and baby Dike on Highland. George Jr. went hunting and fishing with leading New Castle businessmen as well as men from the mill. Like his father, he liked horses and played golf. In the fall of 1921, the golfers of the New Castle Country Club held their first-ever trophy dinner. George Jr. was the toastmaster of the event and also accepted the award for "best ringer score of the season." On April 15, 1922, when the weather was just starting to improve for golfing, a second son was born to George and Hazel. They named him Thomas S. Blair—"S." for both Slingluff and Shoenberger, his enterprising ancestors.

In 1923, George Blair, Jr., followed his father into their new steelmaking venture with confidence. The Blair name carried with it an air of fairness and respectability in New Castle and beyond because of the man George Blair, Sr. was: intelligent, prudent, wise in the ways of finances and business. He was the president of the company but George Jr. was the verve. He held the titles of vice president and treasurer, but more importantly, he was the man who was in the mill each day, gaining the respect of all. When George Blair, Sr., died in April 1928, forty-year-old George Blair, Jr. stepped into the role of president and general manager of Blair Strip Steel. Now it was solely up to him to uphold the Blair business and name.

Under George Jr.'s leadership, Blair Strip Steel continued to thrive and grow. In summer 1929 the company resumed its plans to expand. The new 13,750-square-foot building would house a state-of-the-art cold rolling mill, shears, slitters, and annealing room, all of which were necessary to keep up with the volume of orders coming in.

While times seemed to be good and getting better at Blair, harder times for the American economy—and the American people—lay ahead.

Construction was slow, steel production was declining, and automobile sales were down. Americans were taking on more debt than ever thanks to easy access to boom-time credit. Despite these indicators of economic trouble, the stock market kept rising. Stocks hit record levels during the summer of 1929, and on September 3, 1929, the market hit its peak.

On October 24, 1929—"Black Thursday"—the economic bubble burst and stock prices plummeted. Despite President Herbert Hoover's reassurance that US business was sound, the American people panicked. On October 29, 1929—"Black Tuesday"—the stock market crashed, recording $14 billion in paper losses. It wasn't until nearly a month later that the market hit bottom and began to stabilize. But the damage had been done. The Crash of 1929 marked the beginning of the Great Depression.

While the country faced an unprecedented economic disaster, a catastrophe more immediate threatened Mr. Blair's young company. No one could have seen it coming.

From its earliest days, safety was a priority at Blair Strip Steel. The Blairs knew that preventing accidents was good business from a productivity standpoint, but they also held strongly the belief that the men in the mill should be well protected as they did their jobs. This way of thinking may not seem particularly remarkable now, but a century ago, worker safety was not a focal point in the steel industry or manufacturing industries in general, despite the hazardous nature of the work.

When the plant first opened in August 1924, the company leadership asked the New Castle Fire Department to install a fire hydrant near the building. Fire Chief Charles H. Lynn approved the request, saying a hydrant was "necessary to give the plant adequate fire protection." The Chief's words would prove to be both prophetic and sadly ironic; even a well-placed hydrant was no match for the fire that tore through the mill in the fall of 1930.

Shortly before six a.m. on October 1—not even a year since Black Tuesday—the men working the daytime shift arrived at the mill. It probably felt like any other Wednesday, except that the first game of the World Series would be played later that afternoon. As the men marked their time cards, they may have made petty bets about who would win it all—the "dashing" St. Louis Cardinals or the "formidable" Philadelphia Athletics—or whether President Hoover's ceremonial first pitch would cross the plate as a perfect strike. In a matter of minutes, baseball would be the last thing on their minds.

Shortly after six o'clock, men started yelling. There was a fire in the shipping room. A few of them ran for the in-house fire hose, which may have been connected to the ill-fated hydrant, but the fire moved too swiftly. Flames shot along the roofline then dropped to the floor, forcing the men to abandon the hose and get out of the mill as fast as they could move.

At 6:20, the Central Fire Station in New Castle answered an alarm call from the Blair mill. The exhausted firemen had just finished battling a two-hour blaze on the West Side, but they sped to the East Side to fight the fire at Blair. The units from Central and Firehouse No. 4 arrived just in time to see the flames engulf the wooden roof of the main plant. Two more firefighting units—Nos. 3 and 5—were called in.

The city firemen worked five straight hours to contain the blaze. By midmorning, the roof of the main plant had collapsed. Even after the flames were out, the firemen continued to spray water onto the hot metal supports rising crookedly from the smoldering rubble. "While crowds milled about the scene of the destruction," read the *New Castle News* that night, "George D. Blair, Jr. president of the plant, quietly surveyed the ruins. The holocaust had rendered useless practically every piece of machinery in the building. Some finished products were noticed near the charred embers of what were formerly packing crates."

Indeed, the damage was staggering. The building itself was destroyed, as was most of the equipment in the machine shop, a few of the rolling mills, and an unspecified amount of product that had yet to be shipped. The morning after the fire, Mr. Blair and assistant superintendent Thomas "Tucker" Nolan picked their way through "15,000 square feet of twisted masses of metal, puddles of water and mounds of brick and cement." The material loss was thought to be about $350,000—an amount roughly equivalent in value to $5.4 million in 2020. Most notably, and to the amazement and relief of all, not one Blair employee, firefighter, or bystander was injured.

George Blair knew how much worse the outcome of the fire could have been if the firefighters had not been as swift or persistent. Less than a week after the fire that had delivered a terrible financial blow to his company, Mr. Blair sent a monetary gift to Chief Lynn and his firefighters with the following note:

Please accept the thanks and appreciation of the Blair
Strip Steel Company for the excellent service rendered us

during our fire of October 1. We appreciate the obstacles you encountered that morning and believe that everything possible was done by your department. Kindly accept the enclosed check for $100.00 as a small material token of our appreciation to you and your good men. We understand you have a fund to which the check will be well diverted.

Yours Sincerely,
George D. Blair, Jr.

In Blair Strip Steel's most difficult hour, friends and allies of the company sent telegrams and made phone calls extending help. Other steel manufacturers, including an unnamed neighboring cold-rolled strip mill, offered their services so Blair could fill outstanding orders. George Blair stated publicly that he expected the newer part of the plant (added in 1929) to be back up and running within thirty days. The building itself was only slightly damaged in the fire, and the two tandem mills and other machinery and equipment it housed remained intact.

Mr. Blair and his men started their rebuilding plan immediately. While the company secured the necessary permits and ordered materials for the construction of the new $21,000 "fireproof" brick-and-steel building, work began on repairing the equipment salvaged from the plant, including six massive wooden pickling vats. By December, the bricklayers were building walls, and by mid-month, the construction crew of A.W. Bauman—the same company that had built the original Blair Strip Steel plant—was scrambling to finish the new building to meet the revised but still ambitious deadline. In early January 1931, the new plant was up and operational.

Though the structure of the original building was very nearly a total loss, one architectural element survived the fire. After everything else around it collapsed, the entry door on the west wall of the mill was still standing in its arched frame. At the time of this book's publication, the archway, with its authentic Pennsylvania keystone and wooden brown door, continues to stand and serve as the main entry and exit for mill employees.

The cause of the fire was never discovered, but in the months following the incident there was speculation about whether the water pressure at the site had been adequate enough for fighting such a large fire. Blair leadership had their doubts and requested that New Castle city officials look into increasing the water pressure to the area. The company would do everything it could to be better prepared for an event that no one hoped to experience again.

Over the course of just six years in business (1924–1930), Blair Strip Steel had faced the loss of its founding president, a nationwide economic crisis, and the nearly-complete destruction of its plant. Any of those trials could have meant the end of the company, but its story was only just beginning.

In October 1930—just a few weeks after the fire at Blair and a year to the day after Black Thursday—the most powerful players in the United States steel industry gathered at the Commodore Hotel in New York City for the semiannual meeting of the American Iron and Steel Institute (AISI). The president of the group, Mr. Charles Schwab of Bethlehem Steel, one of the largest steel companies of the time, delivered a rousing speech. He expressed his optimism about the future of business in the US, despite the economic tempest the country was still trying to navigate. He urged his fellow industry leaders not to slash employee wages and to avoid wholesale layoffs. "The steel industry will lead the march to prosperity," Schwab said,

> Progress is born out of the pains of economic adjustment.
> The past twelve months are the first real test we have had of
> our new 'American Prosperity,' by which I mean the basic
> factors underlying our higher standards of living, including
> production and distribution of higher wages. . . . I believe
> that business revival will bring to this country a larger
> measure of prosperity than the American people have ever
> known before.

Schwab's address was meant to soothe the fears of investors and reassure the American public. "Chas. M. Schwab Says Steel Will Lead March to Prosperity," the front page of the *New Castle News* declared. Though not every speaker at the meeting was as optimistic as Schwab, no one expressed dire pessimism, either. It is likely that many of the AISI members knew that things could get worse before they got better, but it is unlikely that any of the seven hundred steel men in the room could foresee how broad and deep the economic trouble would be or could fathom the real-life hardships wage-earning Americans were about to face during the nation's Great Depression.

The numbers tell a tale of disaster both in the steel sector and in the national economy. In 1929, steelmakers operated at about 91 percent of plant capacity and produced 63,205,000 tons of steel. Nationally, the unemployment rate was 3.2 percent. From 1929 to 1932, steel production dropped more than 75 percent, and the national unemployment rate reached almost 24 percent. As the country slid toward the depths of the Depression, steel numbers got worse. In 1932, the industry produced 15,323,000 tons of steel (compared with more than 63 million tons in 1929) and used only 19.9 percent of plant capacity. Of course nationwide numbers don't tell the whole story. The drastic downturn in steel and other manufacturing sectors hurt small cities whose economies depended heavily on industry. In New Castle, as elsewhere in the country, businesses closed, workers lost their jobs, and families lost their homes.

While the largest steel companies in the industry, including Bethlehem and US Steel, and their employees suffered immensely in the first years of the Depression, smaller companies with far fewer employees like Blair Strip Steel were better equipped to weather the brutal economy. Nonetheless, George Blair was forced to lay off some of his workers and cut work hours. He and his family were not among the New Castle residents who had no other choice but to accept relief aid in order to meet their most basic needs. Nevertheless, he was aware that times were excruciating for many people, including the men who worked so loyally for him.

As Christmas approached, Mr. Blair called together the managers of the company to decide when and how long they would shut down the mill for the holidays. As the meeting came to a close, he reached into his pocket and placed some cash in the middle of the table. He asked his managers to do the same and then distribute the money among the men in the mill as a way to help them out at Christmastime while finances were still so lean. On that day a tradition was born, and to this day, Blair employees are given "Christmas Cash" just before the holiday, with the spirit of George Blair's gesture behind it.

While outside forces including the Depression and the fire threatened to throw Blair Strip Steel off-course during the 1930s, the talent inside the company remained its north star. As mill superintendent, Lester L. Lewis managed the steelmaking operations at Blair, but he was also interested in how the steel they produced could be better. In late 1929, Lewis filed a patent for an apparatus that would improve annealing, the process of gradually heating and then cooling steel to soften it and make it less brittle for further processing. Lewis's apparatus increased the ductility of steel (the ability to draw it into cupped shapes and drawn shells, for example) while also decreasing the cost of production and reducing discoloration of the treated metal. On October 7, 1930, Lewis was granted a patent for his apparatus. He was granted two additional patents related improving the annealing process in August 1932 and February 1933.

Lewis's engineering interests extended beyond the mill. He developed a device that would allow an airplane to fly "blind" through fog or clouds. Mounted on the dashboard inside the cockpit was a device that would warn the pilot if the plane began to tilt too much, front to back or toward one side. Lewis also imagined the device could be used in trains to warn engineers as they drove around blind curves. Though Lewis's blind flying device was tested effectively and met with enthusiasm, it appears that Lewis's attempts to officially patent the invention were not ultimately successful.

Blair Strip Steel would ride out the worst of the Depression and survive to see better times. Shortly after Franklin Delano Roosevelt took office in March 1933, Congress authorized the new president to take immediate steps to increase employment and breathe some life into American industry. In spring 1933, Congress adopted the National Industrial Recovery Act (NIRA). It called upon the leaders of the steel industry to establish codes of "fair competition," which allowed businessmen to fix prices and allocate production quotas. The codes also set minimum wages and maximum hours of employment for workers.

In summer 1933, Blair Strip Steel conformed to the new codes by establishing a base compensation rate of forty cents per hour and raising all other wages by fifteen percent, as well as rearranging the schedule of work hours mill-wide. By February 1934, things were looking better at Blair. "We expect to have all our old men back on the job shortly," said a stoutly optimistic George Blair. "We are increasing production every week, orders are increasing, and I feel certain that conditions are definitely on the way up." The following month, steel industry leaders agreed on an additional ten-percent wage increase, which Blair adopted for all its employees.

Because NIRA authorized business leaders to join collectively in self-interest, the American Federation of Labor (AFL) requested the same opportunity for laborers. A new section was written into NIRA, giving workers the right to organize and bargain collectively. The labor movement had been weakened following a failed nationwide steel strike in 1919, but with the new section in NIRA and the conditions of the Depression sharpening the "sense of grievance" among workers, the labor movement again gained momentum. Blair Strip Steel, like many other manufacturers in Western Pennsylvania, would be approached by union organizers in the coming decades.

Blair's fate continued to be tied to the automotive industry throughout the 1930s. Growth in automobile and truck manufacturing slowed during the Depression. From 1930–32, auto production dropped by 75 percent, and steel usage in auto applications dropped almost as much. Fortunately for Blair, the auto industry recovered more quickly than most other industries. By 1937, the automotive sector had recovered its total production to 90 percent of 1929 levels. But automakers and their suppliers were not out of the woods. In 1938, a severe recession cut auto production by almost half, causing a 52 percent drop in steel use and once again slowing steel production. It was a temporary dip, however. In 1940 auto production topped 4 million units—a level the industry had reached only a few times during the Roaring Twenties.

The steel industry was in better shape than the overall US economy during the Depression, but it did not return to its 1929 level of production until 1940. At that point, war demand had become a factor. US steelmakers were supplying materials for the production of aircraft and artillery ordered by the British and French military, which were already engaged in the conflict that would become World War II. When the US entered the war in December 1941, manufacturing took on new urgency. Instead of making passenger vehicles for American motorists, US automakers began to produce military vehicles and the equipment of battle, including transport trucks, artillery, tanks, and aircraft. In February 1942 the sale of passenger vehicles to civilians was halted completely. Wartime needs took precedence over consumer desires.

In 1941 and 1942, Blair set aside most of its regular customers in order to roll heavy gauge steel for army tank bearings produced by Timken of Canton, Ohio. Blair also produced heavy gauge steels with a "corn cob" pattern that would be used in hand grenade bodies and other steel-based war applications.

But not everything Blair made during the war went to the front lines. In appreciation of Blair's wartime service, the federal government awarded the company an order to produce 825 tons of cold rolled strip steel for shipment to the US Treasury. The US Mint planned to make pennies from zinc-coated steel in order to conserve copper for ammunition and wiring. Blair Strip Steel was the sole supplier of the steel for pennies minted for the year 1943. The emergency coinage or "white pennies" remained in circulation until the 1960s. Though they are not as rare or valuable among collectors as 1943 copper pennies, they remain a symbol of how a small company like Blair made a big contribution when called upon. So it remains today that anyone who finds a steel penny holds a sample of Blair strip steel.

———————

In the 1930s, George Blair encouraged his young sons, Dike and Tom, to pursue professional opportunities outside the family business. He told them that cold rolling was a "dying field" and Blair Strip Steel "would never make it." He believed that engineering developments by large, integrated operations like US Steel and Bethlehem Steel would put Blair out of business. There were also broader-scale economic adversities to consider, like the Depression, which had decimated businesses locally and nationally, a reality George Blair had felt acutely as both a business owner and an employer of more than one hundred men. He had witnessed the Great War and saw how it turned whole industries—and societies—upside down. He knew, too, the way fortunes can flip in an instant, like when a fire threatens to destroy your men, your mill, and your livelihood on an unremarkable Wednesday morning. If a man was lucky, really lucky, he got a brief moment to make something of his good fortune, but moments pass. They always pass.

Even more than his company, George Blair cared about the men who made the steel. Fiercely. He cared about their well-being and their families and the community they all shared, company president and laborers alike. George Blair was said to have personally funded the college education and medical school training of a young man in New Castle who showed great promise but didn't have the financial means. The young man went on to establish a well-regarded obstetrics and gynecology practice in Detroit.

In 1947, on behalf of Blair Strip Steel, George Blair pledged $20,000 (roughly $231,000 in 2020 dollars) to the Jameson Memorial Hospital expansion campaign. It was the largest gift from the industrial sector in New Castle. And then George and Hazel Blair gave an additional $5,000 ($57,000 in 2020) as a personal donation. The *New Castle News* mentioned the donations in a story it ran about the hospital project. No doubt Mr. Blair was not consulted on the story, as he would never have approved of the attention. It was not the Blair way. To do good work, to treat people fairly, and to do it all without self-promotion or fanfare— that was the Blair way.

As dignified as George and Hazel Blair appeared publicly, they also possessed a gentleness of spirit and down-to-earth tastes. Hazel loved baseball, in particular the Pittsburgh Pirates. She and George would listen to radio broadcasts together and discuss the nuances of the game. They were New Castle people through and through: hard working, family-centered, and no matter how much they achieved, they were never overly impressed with themselves.

In 1949, while spending time in Arizona to escape the depths of winter, George Blair became ill. He returned home to Moody Avenue in New Castle to rest and recover, but he never regained his strength. In mid-April, George was admitted to Jameson Memorial Hospital for complications of heart disease. He died on May 5 at the age of sixty-one. There was no announcement in the local paper, no obituary, no public memorial service to recognize the life of a man who had accomplished so much and helped so many. It just wasn't his way.

Years after his death, a family member asked Hazel why she never remarried. "Once you've had the best," she said, "why look for another?"

We can only imagine what it was like for Hazel to listen to her Pirates, and later watch them on TV, without George for twenty-eight years. We can only wonder if sometimes, between pitches, her mind wandered along the tracks of memory to a young railroad agent out of South Bend who had no idea what stretched before him—before them—except a length of steel rail and the next tie.

CHAPTER 7

FIFTY YEARS ON TEMPORARY ASSIGNMENT: THE LEADERSHIP OF THOMAS S. BLAIR

Life is a lot like jazz . . . It's best when you improvise.
—George Gershwin,
American composer (1898–1937)

Thomas S. Blair was never supposed to run a steel company. Upon his father's advice about the limited future of the strip steel industry, he built a career and a life elsewhere, a world apart from New Castle, Pa. And yet, in May 1949, days after his father's death, twenty-seven-year-old Tom Blair found himself seated in front of the Blair Strip Steel board of directors, about to be elected president of the company. The board wanted a Blair to take the reins. They felt it was the only way to maintain a sense of order following the loss of a man so deeply and widely respected in the industry and the community and so loved by his employees. Tom agreed to accept the position but only as a temporary assignment; he would keep things going until the right man could be found.

As it happened, Tom Blair himself was the right man. He spent fifty years on that temporary assignment, making sure his family's company not only survived but thrived. Across those five decades, one standard drove his work: that he was running Blair Strip Steel the way his father would have done it, treating everyone—customers, employees, and shareholders—like they mattered. Because to the Blairs, everyone did.

———

Dike and Tom Blair grew up on Highland Avenue in New Castle. Their big yellow-brick house sat at the bottom of a two-block hill where the road curved, making it a prime location for watching the trolley cars, sparks flying from their wheels, warning bells clanging. The boys longed to be the conductor so they could clang the bell and run the car around the curve at top speed. Their front yard was a steep hill and good for sledding, though they had to perfect the art of turning at the last minute to avoid flying onto the busy street. The best sledding spot, though, was a few blocks away. The braver neighborhood boys would help themselves to the bumpers of passing cars for a tow back up the hill. While the motorists weren't too pleased with the kids' ingenuity, the kids themselves didn't see a problem with it.

Every Saturday afternoon, Dike and Tom walked the mile to downtown and watched a cowboy movie at the Regent Theater. "Invariably," according to Dike, they ate Necco Wafers during the show. In the summer, they went swimming in Cascade Park or Neshannock Creek. Every evening at seven o'clock, they listened to *Amos 'n' Andy* on the radio, just like all the households in their neighborhood. The Blair family occasionally took trips to Pittsburgh by car. Their visits usually included a visit to the Carnegie museums and a Pirates game at Forbes Field, where they listened intently as their father explained the subtle plays of the game.

At the age of nine, Dike received a Mysto Magic set for Christmas. From that moment, he was hooked. He became "the boy magician," his interest fed by the magic tricks his father brought home from monthly sales trips to Detroit. Dike first specialized in parlor magic, putting on shows for his parents' friends after dinner parties, and then he moved up to performing platform magic at lunch meetings and in church basements. He attended magic conventions and eventually did some stage magic—a Saturday morning show for kids at the Penn Theater. The boy magician was devoted to his craft into his teenage years, and though he would develop other interests, magic remained a beloved hobby for most of his life.

As young men, both Dike and Tom attended The Hill School in Pottstown, Pennsylvania, but they returned home to New Castle for summers and holidays. Upon finishing high school, Dike went to Williams College in Williamstown, Massachusetts, and Tom followed. Tom was a brilliant student who was interested in his studies, but he got away to New York as often as he could to hear live jazz. He couldn't get enough of it. Sometimes he would sit in a club all night, nursing the one Coca-Cola that a quarter could buy him, just listening to the musicians play.

Before long, Tom Blair was living in the city. He had been recruited away from Williams to work at Columbia University on a top-secret government initiative. The Manhattan Project tapped some of the brightest minds in physics, chemistry, engineering, and manufacturing to help develop the first and only nuclear weapon used in armed conflict to date. Much of the work was carried out under extreme secrecy, and most of the researchers and workers involved did not have a sense of the scope of the project. All they knew was the specific work they performed and that it was not to be talked about with anyone, including others working in the same building.

Though the letter is dated simply "Monday night," it is likely that Tom Blair wrote a letter to his parents on the evening of July 16, 1945, to reflect on the United States' first test detonation of an atomic bomb in New Mexico as part of the Manhattan Project. "Well, the big secret is out," Tom began,

> We were notified that we were now permitted to tell people that we are working on atomic power. But no more. We're to give no newspaper interviews or even to publicly confirm or deny newspaper stories. The why's and wherefore's still have to be kept strictly secret.
>
> Everyone in the lab was naturally pretty excited about the whole thing. I rather wish they'd have waited to see what the effects of the bomb were other than raising a lot of dust before they released any news of it.
>
> I'm very lucky, I think now, to have gotten into a department of the project which really is the key to the whole works. Everything at Oak Ridge is based on and dependent on our particular work. For the first year and a half here [at Columbia], I was more less chasing up blind alleys—methods that never worked out.

Tom went on to apologize to his parents for keeping the nature of his work a secret from them but acknowledged that it was in the best interest of everyone involved that he had. He asked that his parents forward the letter to his brother, Dike, as an apology for denying that he (Tom) was indeed working on a bomb—not a "Uranium bomb," as Dike had guessed, but something different and much more potent.

Tom Blair was aware that the technology he had a part in developing within the Manhattan Project had implications that reached far beyond his lab in New York City. "The thing, needless to say, is really going to change the world," he wrote.

As the most tremendous source of power imaginable,

everything is going to have to be adapted to it. Engineering problems will be terrific, but someday they'll build houses and be able to heat them for as long as they'll stand with about a quarter of a gram of the stuff.

Tom also recognized the peril that came with this new kind of power the United States had invented for itself. Toward the letter's close, he wrote, "Well, it may be the destruction of everything, or it may work out to give the whole world a standard of living far above everything ever known. Let's hope it all comes out all right." A few weeks after Tom wrote those words and sent them to New Castle, the United States would detonate two atomic bombs over Hiroshima and Nagasaki, ending World War II and birthing a new era for the entire world.

In the midst of his top-secret work, Tom Blair's life in New York City continued to unfold. One evening, he called upon a woman named Joan who lived not far from him on the Upper West Side. When he arrived at her apartment, Joan was not ready for the date, and so Joan's sister, Phyllis, took it upon herself to entertain the quiet, handsome young man. According to Phyllis, Joan had been out the previous night and wasn't very interested in Tom, but after Phyllis's conversation with him, Phyllis was.

Tom's and Phyllis's dates included trips to Jones Beach, where they dined on seafood and enjoyed each other's company, lapsing into comfortable silences to avoid the topic of their respective work lives. Like Tom, Phyllis had also left college to do war-related work. First she was as an engineering draftsman for General Electric in Schenectady, executing drawings for secret radar installations. When she met Tom, she was working at Bell Laboratories, rendering detailed illustrations of aircraft. It wasn't long before the couple got married.

In 1946, Tom was transferred from New York to Oak Ridge, Tennessee, to continue his research on processes for separating uranium isotopes. Though the war had ended, the massive facilities in Oak Ridge were still being used for the development of atomic technology. When the Blairs arrived in Oak Ridge, tens of thousands of people were still living and working in the compounds built expressly for Manhattan Project workers and their families. While Tom worked at Oak Ridge, Phyllis taught second and third grade in the hills of nearby Clinton. The poverty of her students and their families was eye opening, as were the differences between their cultural norms and Phyllis's own. When Phyllis showed her students an illustration that depicted Earth as a sphere, she received angry letters from parents forbidding her from teaching their children that the world was round; it was a betrayal of the folk wisdom they were passing down to their children.

After spending a year and a half in Tennessee, the Blairs moved to Peekskill, New York—the only place in the greater metropolitan area where they could find an apartment following the war. Tom worked as associate editor and wrote technical articles for *The Iron Age*, a weekly magazine for the steel industry, and finished his degree from Williams by passing oral exams made especially difficult by the time that had passed since his college coursework. Tom and Phyllis did not imagine leaving New York, but in April 1949, they received word that George Blair was gravely ill. They were needed in New Castle right away.

Though his health had been declining, no one expected the end of George Blair's life to come so quickly. Dike and his wife, Reba, had traveled to New Castle to help care for George in his final days, and so when Tom and Phyllis arrived from New York, both sons were present to make the difficult decisions about how to proceed.

Dike, the older of George and Hazel's two sons, had also pursued a professional life far afield from Blair Strip Steel. After serving stateside during the war, he became a manager in the Doubleday Book Shop chain, first at a store in Grand Central Station in New York and then at the Fisher Building shop in Detroit. In 1949, he opened The Vermont Book Shop in Middlebury, Vermont, to serve—and delight—the population of the small college town. He referred to himself as the "genial prop." and was known for the humorous narrative advertisements he wrote to entice the students of Middlebury College to visit the bookstore, which also sold records. The renowned American poet Robert Frost was a loyal customer of The Vermont Book Shop and a friend of Dike Blair. He claimed that Dike could read his mind and always knew exactly which book he'd come in for.

While Dike was not interested in managing the operations of Blair Strip Steel, he agreed to become involved in the business as a member of the board of directors when Tom took over. The board met five times a year, and early in his tenure, Dike didn't always make it to the meetings. His mother, Hazel, and Tom both knew he could be an important contributor, so they encouraged him to make his attendance a priority. And so he did. Dike traveled from Middlebury to New Castle five times a year for sixty-one years and let his voice and sensibilities help guide his family's company. He was also an active leader in his own industry and community.

From 1970 to 1984, Dike Blair was a director and officer in the American Booksellers' Association, and he served on several boards in Middlebury. His enthusiasms were many, and his spirit was indomitable. "I'm not afraid to die," he once said, "but I have too much to do."

Whether it was ever something the brothers discussed remains unknown, but Tom needed Dike's support in his new role as the head of Blair Strip Steel. The first few years were especially daunting. Tom Blair was an intelligent, insightful leader and a quick study; still, he was only twenty-seven years old and just starting out as the lead decision-maker of a steel company. Union organizers may have seen his youth and inexperience as an opportunity. Before Tom Blair had been president for even two years, his employees faced intense pressure to unionize. In a difficult, unfamiliar situation, the young leader relied on one of his tried and true skills: writing. Tom Blair wrote a series of letters to his employees, addressing questions about what the union was proposing and what it might mean for Blair workers. He encouraged his employees to consider the facts presented by the union and by the company and then urged them to, above all else, have a say in deciding their future:

> You <u>should</u> vote—one way or the other. And you can feel perfectly free in voting for either side. <u>No one</u>, not even the National Labor Relations Board, will know how you, as an individual, vote. . . .
>
> Just be <u>sure</u> you vote. You and your family have a personal stake in the outcome of the election.
>
> Cordially,
> Thomas S. Blair

The letters reached his employees on a personal level and calmed their anxieties. Ultimately, the employees of Blair Strip Steel voted not to unionize.

Retirees of Blair Strip Steel who remember those tense times recall Tom Blair's poise as he handled the pressure. Through tough times and good times, "Mr. Blair" had a way of making a person feel like he was just as important to the company as the president himself. He was known for his fair treatment of his employees and his inspirational performance reviews. "Tom would chew your ass out and you'd leave his office feeling good about it," one retiree remembered with fondness.

More than his intelligence or even his admirable leadership, those who knew Tom Blair tell stories about his genuine humility, like the time he was spotted picking up litter outside the Blair main office. Or the time his dark green Buick Park Avenue—and he always drove a dark green Buick Park Avenue—was in for repairs and he was given a big luxury car as a loaner, which he immediately returned for a tiny Ford.

So many of those who worked with Tom Blair or for him describe him as "a real gentleman." He had an air of seriousness and refined manners, but he also didn't take himself too seriously. He had a good sense of humor and valued his leisure time, which included listening to his extensive collection of jazz recordings, playing golf, and getting together with other New Castle families for picnics and tureen dinners. It was a known fact that Tom Blair could beat you at any sport that required a racquet. He'd played squash competitively in college and grew up on tennis, playing it and racquetball throughout his adulthood. He'd even mastered badminton. Tom's son, Hadden, can't remember ever beating his dad at the sport.

Though Tom Blair was a Pittsburgh Steelers fan, he played golf several times with Cleveland Browns head coach Paul Brown. Tom Blair came to appreciate and admire how Brown ran his team like a business, and over time, the two developed a friendship. Tom Blair became a Browns season ticket holder in 1952. As sacrilegious as it may sound to some fans, to this day Blair Strip Steel remains a season ticket holder for both the Cleveland Browns and the Pittsburgh Steelers.

Mr. Blair knew his employees enjoyed their leisure time, too, so he strove for both efficiency and fairness; everyone deserved a little time off and some money to spend in it. Though there was a general air of respect and formality in the office, there was always time for geniality and friendliness. Mr. Blair himself would ask around the office on Fridays to see who wanted to play the horses, and he'd call the numbers in himself. Hadden Blair remembers going to the racetrack with his dad and his dad's friends as a boy. It was young Hadden's job to place the bets at the window and bring back the tickets to the men, hoping he'd kept all the numbers straight. Like his father and grandfather, Tom Blair had an affinity for horses, for harness racing in particular. He enjoyed handicapping and owned some horses of his own, many of which he bought at claiming races. It was an interest he shared with some of his New Castle friends, one of whom built a harness track upon retirement.

In 2003, about twenty years after he stepped away from the position of president of Blair Strip Steel and almost four years after he retired from his role as chairman of the board, Tom Blair died of heart failure near his home in Boynton Beach, Florida. The morning he fell ill, he'd been planning to go watch his horses at the track.

Tom Blair's legacy reaches far beyond the work he did on behalf of Blair Strip Steel, its employees, and their families. He cared deeply about the New Castle community and continued the service and philanthropy that his father and grandfather had begun from the moment they arrived in town. Quietly, modestly, Tom and Phyllis Blair and the extended Blair family gave to the hospital, the YMCA, and arts organizations in the city. The Blairs also gave of their time and talents. Tom Blair was a longtime director of the Columbia Gas System in Pennsylvania and a number of other corporations and institutions, including The First National Bank of Lawrence County—the same bank his grandfather, George D. Blair, Sr., directed until his death.

While living in New Castle, Phyllis Blair devoted countless hours toward her work as a trustee and the Art Chair for the Hoyt Institute of Fine Arts. She also volunteered for the New Castle Hospital and its Almira Home, the Lawrence County Children and Youth Services, and a local soup kitchen near the Blairs' home in Florida. She earned many accolades for her service, including the Benjamin Rush Award from the Lawrence County Medical Society and the American Heart Association's Distinguished Service Award.

Phyllis Blair was never the kind to sit back and be a figurehead, however. She always got things done, no matter the task. Blair board member George Weingartner recalled waiting on Mrs. Blair at his family's garden shop over the years. "She was the kind of person who picked up her own fertilizer," Weingartner said. "Maybe she even applied it herself. I think she borrowed a spreader once."

Long before she became an illustrator for GE during World War II, Phyllis Emmerich Blair was making art. Her paternal grandmother was an artist and gave Phyllis her first set of oil paints at age twelve. One of Phyllis's earliest works was a rendering of an old barn near her grandmother's home in Hazleton, Pennsylvania. Phyllis became an accomplished visual artist in a variety of media, including watercolor, oil, and acrylic paint as well as marble sculpture. She was a prolific creator and has exhibited her work in a variety of galleries and spaces in several states, including the Butler Institute of American Art in Salem, Ohio, and the Ann Norton Sculpture Gardens in Palm Beach, Florida. She maintained a studio near her home in Williamstown, Massachusetts, until 2015. After more than seventy years of making art, Phyllis Blair died in July 2019. She was ninety-six years old.

Tom and Phyllis Blair are survived by their children, Joan Dix Blair, Dike Blair, and Hadden Blair, each of whom is continuing the Blair legacy of creativity and generosity. Hadden Blair has served on the board of Blair Strip Steel since 2003.

Everyone who knew Tom Blair knows that he would be uncomfortable with a book praising the Blair family and Blair Strip Steel; self-promotion just isn't the Blair way. However, Tom Blair did want the history of a company like Blair to be told. He saw the value in telling the story of how a small steelmaker handled adversity and how, through eight generations, a family has passed on the gifts and upheld the responsibilities entrusted to them. In these times, which seem to celebrate self-aggrandizement and self-interest, it's worth recognizing an American family who has conducted business in the way the Blairs have done and continue to do: with humility, and as if people matter.

Beth Lysinger and Jim
Stillwagon, December 14, 1999
Blair Strip Steel Company

(front l to r) Dave Williams, Glen Lutz, Bill Gibson, Bill Foreman, (back l to r) Darrell
Montgomery, and Bob Harry celebrate Glen Lutz's retirement at Tall Cedars of Lebanon on
June 10, 1991. *Darrell Montgomery*

(standing l to r) Nancy Williams, Larry Wimer, Glenn Turner, Jim Stillwagon, Karen Ippolito, Dick Black, Tucker Nolan, Ken Harris, and (seated) Bill Nulph enjoy a Blair Super Bowl party in January 1979. *Glenn Turner*

"New guys" Scott McDowell and Bruce Kinney at the Christmas celebration in the Blair main office in December 1999 *Blair Strip Steel Company*

BLAIR
WALL OF FAME

Blair President and CEO Bruce Kinney with his wife, Karen "Peeps" Kinney (left), and Sarah Jayne Kinney in front of the Blair "Wall of Fame" at the party celebrating Blair's 90th birthday in August 2013 *Blair Strip Steel Company*

Inventory of raw, hot-rolled coils ready for cold rolling on Blair's tandem reduction mills *Blair Strip Steel Company*

Andy Duggan (left) and Gary Campbell load a coil of steel on the small slitter, which will cut the steel down to a narrower width. *Blair Strip Steel Company / Whitney Tressel, 2017*

Roller John Jopek sets up the "Little Tom" mill before he rolls a coil. *Blair Strip Steel Company / Whitney Tressel, 2017*

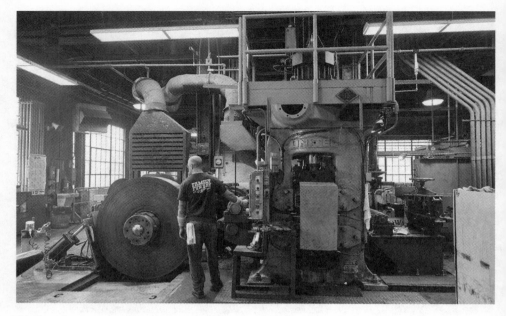

Ed Sheridan operates "Big George," the larger of Blair's two rolling mills, named in honor of company founders George D. Blair and George D. Blair, Jr. *Blair Strip Steel Company / Whitney Tressel, 2017*

Dave Fletcher stacks coils of steel and moves annealing furnaces by remote control. *Blair Strip Steel Company / Whitney Tressel, 2017*

A trucker secures coils of finished steel to ship to Blair customers. *Blair Strip Steel Company / Whitney Tressel, 2017*

Exterior shot of the Blair Strip Steel plant, 2020 *Blair Strip Steel*

Constructed in 1924, the Blair Strip Steel plant has remained in its original location on Butler Avenue on the east side of New Castle. *Blair Strip Steel Company, 2016*

Bruce Kinney holds the first Belleville disc spring to come off the line at BelleFlex Technologies in 2010. *Blair Strip Steel Company*

Bruce Kinney carries on the tradition of greeting retirees and employees at the Blair Christmas celebration in 2017. *Blair Strip Steel Company / Whitney Tressel*

Blair employee Dave Fletcher (back left) and retiree Dan Cullen (front left) are greeted by Scott McDowell and Beth Lysinger to begin the Christmas celebration at the mill in 2017. *Blair Strip Steel Company / Whitney Tressel*

Blair employees and retirees gather for the annual Christmas celebration at the mill in 2017. *Blair Strip Steel Company / Whitney Tressel*

Hadden Blair and Phyllis Blair visit with Alex Lultschik at the 90th birthday celebration for Blair Strip Steel in August 2013. *Blair Strip Steel Company*

Members of the Blair family gathered at Blair Strip Steel in August 2013 for the dedication of the flagpole memorial for Tom Blair. Pictured are (left to right) Michael Johnson, Susan (Blair) Johnson, Jodi Blair, Hadden Blair, Phyllis Blair, Joan Blair, Malcolm Wyer, and Dike Blair. *Blair Strip Steel Company*

Phyllis E. Blair made art throughout her life, including this painting titled *Ballet* (1972). A longtime friend of the New Castle YMCA, Phyllis gave the painting to the downtown Y, where it remains on exhibit today. *Lawrence County YMCA*

Aerial shot of Blair Strip Steel taken on September 25, 1956. *Blair Strip Steel Company*

(l to r) Bonnie Bardash, Lisa Book, Karen Ippolito, Carole Sheen, and Beth Lysinger pose with president Jim Stillwagon at the Blair main office in the late 1990s. *Blair Strip Steel Company*

In the early decades of Blair Strip Steel, cold-rolled steel was heated for further processing in box annealing furnaces like these. Several men would load a heavy plate of steel coils onto "cannon balls" and roll the plate into the sweltering furnace. Days later, the furnace gang would shoulder leather straps and pull the cooled steel back out. *Glenn Turner*

Blair Strip Steel updated its annealing department in the late 1970s, which included constructing an addition tall enough to accommodate modern bell furnaces. *Glenn Turner*

Memorial flagpole for Tom Blair (left), Blair Strip Steel plant (center), Blair main offices (right) in 2020 *Blair Strip Steel Company*

1,800 fiberglass strands feed into #4 Pultrusion Line at PulFlex Technologies. *Blair Strip Steel Company*

Phyllis E. Blair at the Blair Strip Steel 90th birthday celebration in August 2013
Blair Strip Steel Company

BelleFlex employee Rameshwar Narine with his wife and daughter, BelleFlex General
Manager Ben Kessing, and PulFlex Vice President-Operations Craig Lawson at the PulFlex
plant in Ford City in August 2019 *Blair Strip Steel Company*

Logo for BelleFlex Technologies, LLC. The Blair "outrigger" business was founded in 2009 to engineer custom disc springs for challenging industrial applications. *Blair Strip Steel Company*

Logo for PulFlex Technologies, founded in 2018 as a subsidiary of BelleFlex Technologies to produce high-quality fiberglass and carbon fiber pultrusions *Blair Strip Steel Company*

Founding BelleFlex general manager Frank Ballina poses with a 42-inch Belleville disc spring. *Blair Strip Steel Company*

Box of Belleville disc springs manufactured at BelleFlex Technologies in Ford City, PA. *Blair Strip Steel Company*

Dave Pastore served Blair for 14 years as Virtual Processing Manager before falling ill with COVID-19 and passing away in March 2020. *Blair Strip Steel Company*

CFO Scott McDowell talks with longtime employees Pat Schooley and Marty Post at the Blair Christmas celebration in 2009. In 2019, McDowell was named President of Blair Strip Steel. *Blair Strip Steel Company*

Kevin Barren (left) replaced John Avau as Vice President of Operations when John retired in December 2013 after 27 years at Blair. *Blair Strip Steel Company, 2009*

CHAPTER 8

MAKING IT:
BLAIR STRIP STEEL
1949–1999

During the thirty years that the name BLAIR has been synonymous with quality cold rolled strip steel, the foreman of each operation has been charged with the responsibility of careful, conscientious inspection. Thus, material improperly pickled could not be cold rolled: if not correctly cold rolled, would never reach the annealing department—and so on throughout each stage of production. This system results in a mere fraction of one percent of actual customer rejection in any single year. . . . This chain of progressive inspection is unique and ensures satisfaction.

—from a Blair Strip Steel sales brochure, ca. 1954

In the years following World War II, the US led the world in steel production. Despite George Blair's misgivings about the future of the strip industry, it was a profitable time to be an American steelmaker. When Tom Blair took over the company in 1949, Blair Strip Steel was in very good shape.

As orders streamed in, longtime mill superintendent Thomas "Tucker" Nolan made sure his men were up keeping up. Tucker was old school. He had begun working at Blair in 1927 as a "Push-n-Puller" with the furnace gang and quickly became the heart and the hammer of the steelmaking operation. He was known for saying, "I don't know if I'm hiring today or firing today." He pushed his guys hard and held them to a high standard. With five minutes left in a shift, he would walk the floor and make sure his men were still working, and if they weren't, he would dock their pay. He didn't hold back on workers who were lazy or complained. He was a tough boss but fair.

Tucker wasn't exactly sold on Tom Blair at first. Sure, he was Mr. Blair's son and college educated and hand-picked by the government to work on the Bomb, but he was just a kid—a kid who, Tucker was certain, didn't know the first thing about running a steel company. As far as Tucker was concerned, Tom could never measure up to George Blair, Jr., the man Tucker would have taken a bullet for, the greatest man Tucker had ever known.

Though Tucker made it hard on Tom Blair initially, over time their relationship improved. Tom had a way of proposing changes such that they became Tucker's idea. It was an approach that went a long way in deferring to Tucker's experience and staying off the superintendent's toes.

The late 1950s and '60s continued to be good for the steel business. Following World War II and the Korean War, the US economy was growing. The demand for steel was high and rising higher. Blair's business model had not changed much since the company was formed in 1923, nor did it have to, given the demand for strip and minimal import pressure. Blair was able to rely on one product—heavy gauge strip steel—with great success.

Though business was solid, other challenges tested the company and its leadership. By the early 1950s, labor unions had become the dominant force in the steel industry of Western Pennsylvania. Following the unsuccessful unionization attempts in 1951, Blair Strip Steel was again a focus for union organizers in 1953. The pressure on Blair was more aggressive this time. Organizers attempted to disrupt the mill's ability to receive raw materials and ship finished products. But again, the Blair employees voted not to unionize.

Orders for Blair strip from companies like Timken, General Motors, and Ford flooded into the little white house that served as the company's main office. Blair salesmen Jack Allen, Bill Cody, Robert "Tut" Mills, and Tom Van Driel spent much of their time calling on the Detroit automakers. Each came to Blair with engineering and metallurgical knowledge, which allowed them to provide a valuable service. When a customer had a special request, they didn't have to send for a metallurgist. Instead, in the words of Jack Allen, "I just had to call the plant to see how fast we could get it." This was an early glimpse of how Blair was different from its competitors. The company was knowledgeable, nimble, and efficient enough to handle custom orders.

To a certain extent, titles and roles in the main office were inconsequential. Every person learned every job and pitched in wherever he or she was needed. As Glenn Turner, who started his thirty-five-year career at Blair in 1963, put it, "You could be typing orders one minute and the next be over in shipping helping make tags for the steel and doing billing. It was like one big family." Other longtime Blair employees including Dick Black, Ken Harris, Julie (Solomon) Hupko, Karen Ippolito, Francis Morrissey, Bill Nulph, Francis "Red" Sowersby, and Chuck Ward also mastered the art of wearing many hats and doing what needed to be done to keep the office end of things (purchasing, receiving, shipping, billing) running as smoothly and productively as the mill itself. Karen, who was originally hired to be Tom Blair's secretary, took dictation and typed so quickly and mastered so many other skills in the main office that she became known throughout the company as "the girl with ten hands."

Times were good at Blair Strip Steel in the late 1960s and early '70s. The major automakers were thriving, which provided a level of confidence and security for their steel suppliers, including Blair. General foreman Jim Perry and turn foremen Angelo Vitto and Edward "E.J." Kelly kept the mill running three shifts a day, seven days a week. The desire to meet and surpass production goals was contagious. The mill workers' production was tracked, posted, and rewarded with ample overtime pay and eye-popping year-end bonuses.

Blair stored its raw materials offsite with a trucking company that would haul the hot-rolled coils to the mill as they were needed. In an effort to make the steel more immediately accessible when a rush order came in, the company built an onsite warehouse in 1965. A few houses along Cascade Street were torn down to accommodate the new warehouse. Among them was the childhood home of foreman Angelo Vitto, a fact that made him arguably the most "local" Blair employee of all. Another family on the block was the Iafrats. For decades, John Iafrat and then his son, John, worked as outside contractors for Blair. Since their house was next door to the new warehouse, the Iafrats would accept and unload incoming steel, day or night. If a truck brought a load after business hours, the trucker would blow his horn as he entered the driveway adjacent to the Iafrats' house and John would get out of bed and go unload the truck. Since Blair paid by the load, it was a satisfactory arrangement for both parties.

With an endless gush of orders and the steel boom still booming, there was little impetus in the late 1960s and early '70s to make major capital improvements to the mill or its operations. The steelmaking technology at Blair had not changed much since the mill opened in 1924. The incoming hot-rolled steel was still prepared for cold rolling by "pickling" the coils in baths of sulfuric acid, and the annealing process was still being done in box annealing furnaces instead of in more modern bell furnaces. After all, what wasn't broke didn't need fixing.

Until something did break. It wasn't anything in the mill that gave out, however. It was the steel market itself. For years, the demand for steel was higher than what steel companies could supply, which drove prices ever higher and made for hefty profits. The pricing of US steel appeared to be based on the costs of steel, yet following the steel strikes of the late 1950s, Japanese steel poured into the US market, providing a cheaper alternative to domestic steel and marking the beginning of the end. Some say the peak of the steel market came in 1969, while others believe that 1973–74 was the best year. In either case, by the close of 1974 the steel boom was over. 1975 was a sobering year for steelmakers. Companies were forced to reexamine their positions and make decisions accordingly.

Tom Blair recognized that updating the mill was imperative for keeping Blair Strip Steel viable in the long run. In the late 1970s, Blair upgraded to a modern annealing facility, installing several bell furnaces to replace the outmoded box furnaces. The move boosted production and enhanced the quality of Blair's products. More broadly, the change moved the mill out of the "dark ages" of steelmaking and helped the company's chances to remain a contender into the future.

In the 1980s, steelmaking became increasingly automated. Going away were the days of men physically performing every task in the mill; arriving was an era of technical innovation and enhanced integration—for the steel sector generally and for the small but mighty strip mill on Butler Avenue as well. In the mid-1980s, Blair adopted automatic gauge controls on its rolling mills. The technology allowed very precise tolerances without manual adjustment, which decreased scrap loss and increased production.

Besides updates to the mill, Tom Blair knew that other changes needed to happen to keep Blair competitive. He believed the company needed a new leader to guide it into the new era of steelmaking, someone with Big Steel experience and deep knowledge of the industry. He thought he knew just the man to do it.

In February 1984, Tom Blair changed his role to chairman of the board and hired J. Austin Murphy to serve as the president of Blair Strip Steel. "Murph" was an all-star type. He'd built a successful career with US Steel, becoming well respected and well liked throughout the industry. Given his background in Big Steel, he was accustomed to entertaining important customers lavishly. Though Blair had its share of large, influential customers and was a highly successful company in its own right, the move from the United States Steel Corporation to Blair Strip Steel must have been like going from an armored battleship to a handcrafted schooner. Both were formidable vessels, but the two had very different purposes and functions. Ultimately, Austin Murphy resigned from Blair in fall 1989, after four years as president. While Murphy's ideas about moving Blair into the future were sound, his timing and ability to execute them were not successful.

During Murphy's tenure, though, he made a crucial hiring decision based on his extensive industry knowledge and strong relationships with Blair's key customers. Quality control was one of Murphy's priorities, and so upon a colleague's recommendation, he hired John Avau, a young salesman who held a degree in metallurgy. Like Jack Allen and many other Blair employees past and present, John Avau had spent the beginning of his career at big steel companies and never felt they were the right fit for him. Blair ended up being the right place for John, and he arrived at just the right time. Steelmaking was in the midst of evolving from a "heat and beat it" business into an industry that required technological knowledge and skills. Blair needed someone who had experience in sales and also understood the increasingly nuanced orders that were coming in. Although John was brought on as a salesman, he also served as the company's first in-house metallurgist.

As changes took hold in the mill and on the sales front, so business operations in the main office changed. Beth Lysinger started work at Blair in 1983 in the accounting department. It was considered a front office job, and yet during her first few weeks, Beth asked a question that surprised her bosses: "Can I see the mill?" Few, if any, office employees had shown interest in getting to know the mill side of the business firsthand. The administrative and steelmaking worlds at Blair had always operated as separate spheres. There was even a hedge on the Blair property that served as a metaphorical, if not an actual, barrier between the office and the mill.

But every facet of the business was changing. Customers were beginning to ask for specific thicknesses, gauges, and alloys, and so the office and the mill had to communicate both more frequently and more effectively to ensure that customers' needs were being met. The shift from two autonomous parts to an integrated whole was not without its bumps; trust was not built in a day. It helped that employees like Beth, who wanted to know how the mill worked so she could grasp the bigger picture of the company, and John Avau, who knew both the sales and metallurgy sides of the business, had faith that the changes would pay off.

As the story goes, Beth and John were responsible for bringing the Computer Age to Blair's main office. When Beth arrived in 1983, the company had an IBM Personal Computer, but it wasn't doing anything except catching dust. She fired it up and used the spreadsheet program Lotus 1-2-3 to help manage the company's financial records. On the whole, the office remained a pencil-and-paper shop, but useful advances in technology worked their way in a little at a time.

After Austin Murphy left Blair Strip Steel in October 1989, Jim Stillwagon took over as president. Stillwagon had first done auditing work for the company as a public accountant and then was hired at Blair in 1972. A highly respected addition to the organization, Stillwagon served as chief financial officer for several years, including during his tenure as president. To some of his colleagues, Jim was "a breath of fresh air." He was less conservative than august Mr. Blair, though he followed the chairman's vision for the company closely. Jim Stillwagon was himself a gentleman and dressed formally, ever dapper in a suit and tie.

In the early 1990s, Tom Blair saw the end of Blair Strip Steel on the horizon. Despite updating the mill and bringing in new talent to help the company evolve and stay competitive, the future was not promising. The consolidation of the domestic steel industry that had begun in the late 1970s was continuing at a rapid pace. Between 1995 and 2001, dozens of steelmakers would go bankrupt. It meant the shocking end of several well-known corporations, including Bethlehem Steel and LTV Steel, which had acquired Jones & Laughlin and Youngstown Sheet and Tube in the seventies and merged with Youngstown-based Republic Steel in the eighties. The strip steel industry, too, was not immune to consolidation and dissolution. In 1972, there were twenty-six strip producers in the US, and in 2020, only seven remain.

Tom Blair's father had created Blair Strip Steel on the bet that the fledgling automotive industry would soar, and for almost seventy years, it did. In the decades following World War II, two customers, General Motors and Ford, accounted for 70 percent of Blair's sales. Fortunately for Blair, GM and Ford were thriving at that time. But by the 1990s, both previously untouchable automakers were starting to show evidence of financial instability. What's more, the trend toward using less steel in automobiles was growing. Fewer steel components made for lighter, more fuel-efficient vehicles. Automakers found they could replace low-carbon steels with alloy and higher-strength specialty steels and achieve greater strength while reducing weight.

As if the shake-ups happening in the commodity and strip-steel industries in the late 1990s were not ominous enough, Tom Blair saw the turnover that was about to happen within his company's walls. The list of upcoming retirements was long and included several of his most trusted managers: Glenn Turner (who had taken over as mill superintendent in the early 1980s), Dick Black, Jim Stillwagon, and nearly the entire board of directors. He'd already watched the first wave go in the eighties. Tucker Nolan had retired in 1983, followed by Tut Mills and then Jack Allen, though Tucker stayed on as a member of the board. Even Tom himself, despite technically retiring when Austin Murphy was brought on in 1984, thought he might finally be ready to step away from the role of chief decision-maker.

There was also the reality that his children had pursued careers and interests outside the steel business, which was what he had hoped for them. He never wanted to pressure them to get involved. But this also meant Tom would be the last of the Blairs to run the company.

Maybe it was time. They'd had a very good run, after all. The temporary assignment Tom had accepted when his father passed away five decades prior had grown into something well beyond the scope of his own—and his father's—imaginings. Somehow he'd made a whole career out of minding his father's company, the very one that would never make it. Somehow he'd found a way for the company to keep making it.

And so, while the place still had good sale value, maybe it was time to call it a day.

Not that it was an easy decision. It was no small thing to hand over what his family had built to new owners who, as in any business venture, would run it as they saw fit. But it would be a clean break, and selling would be a way to take care of the family and the Blair shareholders.

In the end, Tom Blair wanted to make the wisest decision, just as his father would have done, just as his grandfather, who had decided to split from Elliott-Blair, and his great-grandfather, who had known when to close Blair Iron and Steel, had done. It would be foolish to hold on too long.

So he decided to do the smart thing and let go.

CHAPTER 9

EVOLUTION NOT REVOLUTION: BLAIR STRIP STEEL SINCE 1999

Any intelligent fool can make things bigger, more complex,
and more violent. It takes a touch of genius—and a lot of
courage to move in the opposite direction.
—E.F. Schumacher, 1973

In January 1999, Bruce Kinney agreed to take a job interview with
a headhunter based in New York. It wasn't the sort of thing Kinney
usually did. He was forty-two years old and a vice president at Cold
Metal Products, a strip steel company in Northeast Ohio, and until
that point, Kinney had been unequivocally devoted to his job. But by the
end of 1998, it had become clear to Kinney that he needed to be at a place
that was better aligned with his professional values and his philosophy of
what makes a company both successful and good.

In a hotel conference room near the Pittsburgh airport, the headhunter
laid out the opportunity for Kinney: There was a steel plant in Western
Pennsylvania that was about to be purchased by an investment firm
headquartered in Manhattan, and the firm wanted Kinney to run it.
Though the interviewer never named the steel company, Kinney recognized
certain descriptors and wondered if the place wasn't Blair Strip Steel in
New Castle. He knew of Blair and was aware that it had been around—and
successful—for a long time. He remained interested in the job.

A few interviews and flights to New York later, Kinney was offered
the job at the unnamed steel company. Before he accepted, he reviewed
the company's financial documents to get a clearer picture of what he was
committing to. The carefully prepared book showed Kinney what he was
looking for and more. The name of the steel company had been redacted
or replaced with the generic name "Company X" in almost every place but
one. An oversight, surely, but there it was, in black and white: *Blair*. His

hunch had been correct. Kinney confirmed that the company was indeed Blair Strip Steel and took the job.

Weeks passed. Though the terms of the sale of Blair Strip Steel had been agreed upon and all the legal work was nearly buttoned up, the investment firm had yet to finalize it. One day in March, a partner in the firm called Kinney and said that Tom Blair wanted to meet him; would Kinney do them a favor and meet with Mr. Blair? Kinney was happy to. On a personal level, he was excited by the chance to meet Tom Blair, a man who was respected in the industry but because he kept such a low profile was also a bit of a mystery.

The two met for lunch in downtown New Castle at La Dolce Vita. Upon arriving, Tom Blair apologized for having to keep their meeting brief, as he had another commitment in about an hour's time. They talked about the strip industry, Kinney's experience running a new mill for his previous company, his overall business philosophy, and what plans Kinney had for Blair. Three hours after they'd first sat down, Tom Blair and Bruce Kinney shook hands and parted ways.

Two weeks later, Kinney received a call from Jim Stillwagon, the president of Blair Strip Steel, who asked if Kinney would consider running the company if Tom Blair decided not to sell. The question was unexpected, but it confirmed what Kinney had intuited during their lunch meeting: Even if selling the company made business sense, Mr. Blair's heart wasn't fully into it.

In April 1999, Kinney was hired as the new president of Blair Strip Steel and would officially start in August. That summer, Tom Blair introduced Kinney to the Blair board of directors and invited him to address the group. Kinney was at least twenty years younger than anyone else in the room. In retrospect, he knows how the situation must have looked to the board members, some of whom, including Tucker Nolan, had been working at Blair longer than Kinney had been alive. They must have thought, *here comes this young guy, who no one else but Tom Blair has actually met, and he's full of ideas about what Blair needs to do to stay competitive.* All this after they had just begun to accept the reality that the company was being sold to an outside investor. Deciding not to sell and instead bringing in Kinney was a surprising move, to say the least. But Tom Blair's change of heart and belief in Kinney's vision for the company would prove to be a good move, indeed the right move, for the long-term viability of Blair Strip Steel.

Early in Kinney's tenure at Blair, he recognized the most significant threat to the company's viability: Blair was overexposed to its biggest customers. Unlike the market price for commodity steel, for example, which no one could control, this was a threat that was in the company's power to defuse. Instead of one or two customers comprising half the company's sales, Blair could work to create a stable of eight to ten medium-sized customers that would account for a much smaller percentage of total sales. The approach could reduce significantly Blair's dependence on its largest customers.

With this goal in mind, Kinney devised a five-year plan that included ending an eighty-one-year relationship with General Motors. This strategy was a fairly radical idea and carried real risk. After all, GM had been a customer since the beginning and for much of Blair's history, its biggest, most lucrative customer. By analyzing GM's financial health, Kinney was able to convince those board members who were skeptical of his strategy that reducing, and if necessary eliminating, Blair's reliance on the automaker improved the stability of Blair's customer base and was a step in the direction of longer-term viability. An evolution was underway.

In addition to changing its customer base, Blair's new strategy also called for changing its product mix. Prior to 1999, Blair produced mostly low-carbon, fairly generic varieties of cold-rolled steel for use in automotive applications, including window regulators—the crank mechanism that raised and lowered windows prior to electric windows—and transmission components. Following Kinney's five-year plan, Blair began to specialize in high-carbon and custom grades of steel and alloys. As one Blair manager put it, "We don't make plain vanilla; we make fudge ripple." Today, Blair's specialty steel is used in seating, safety, closure, steering, and engine components. Prior to 1999, the manufacture of steel for five automotive parts made up 25 percent of Blair's business. In 2020, forty to fifty parts make up a quarter of Blair's business. The rest of their business includes specialty steel used in electrical, aircraft, industrial, hardware, stamping, and fineblanking applications, many of which are produced to European or Japanese specifications.

To evolve successfully, Blair needed to increase its metallurgical knowledge and expertise. Plant manager and chief metallurgist John Avau was tasked with learning a massive amount of new information and implementing the knowledge and techniques in the mill. Avau's trust in Kinney's vision for the business and Kinney's trust in Avau's steel intelligence would prove to be the difference between Blair remaining fruitlessly in the past and changing judiciously so it could have a future. In addition, the arrival of Gordon Wilber, a retired metallurgist with a

PhD from Rensselaer Polytechnic Institute and a long, successful career in specialty strip steel, proved to be a valuable resource for Avau as he guided the mill operation toward specialization. In the following years, the expertise of several more Blair metallurgists, including John Moroco, Lou Todora, Kevin Barren, Ivan Clark, Dan Emanuele, and Dominic Sikora, helped Blair shift from producing generic grades of steel to specialty grades and maintain a reputation for making strip of the highest quality.

With the increase in specialty and highly customized orders, effective internal communication became more crucial than ever. Long gone were the days when the office and the mill were divided by the metaphorical hedge. Kinney's leadership style encouraged open communication among departments and the sharing of vital information. It built trust among employees and managers and served the company especially well as changes were gradually introduced.

While it was Kinney who laid the path for Blair's evolution, it was Scott McDowell who helped galvanize the company as it made its way forward. A native of Butler, Pennsylvania, and a graduate of Grove City College, McDowell had finance and accounting experience at both large and small firms. He wanted to stay true to his Western Pennsylvania roots as well as continue to grow his knowledge of manufacturing, so when the opportunity at Blair came up in 1999, it seemed like the way to do both.

Just six months after McDowell was hired, the company was headed in a new direction with a new president leading the way. McDowell shared Kinney's vision for Blair and supported his "evolution, not revolution" approach to making strategic changes; he was willing to do whatever it took for the long-term success of Blair. In addition to his duties as controller, McDowell agreed to become Blair's first quality control manager. He was a quick study of Blair's operations, products, customers, and the strip industry overall as he handled customer claims and maintained Blair's automotive quality system certifications. In short order McDowell became chief financial officer of Blair Strip Steel and joined the Blair board of directors in 2004. Though he served the company well in both roles, they weren't the last positions McDowell would hold at Blair. Down the road, the company would call upon his leadership again as it continued to evolve.

During the first fifteen years of Kinney's tenure, the mill operation underwent several crucial updates. The plant's primary cold-rolling mill has the distinction of producing the heaviest-gauge strip steel in the world. It was acquired in the 1940s and was likely a two-stand mill at first, with a third stand added in 1953 during Tom Blair's tenure. In 2007 it was upgraded and computerized. Around the same time it was officially named "Big George" in honor of company founders George D. Blair and George D. Blair, Jr.

Blair hired a leading metals engineering company to modernize Big George, but Kinney also brought in an additional expert to oversee the process. Earlier in his career, Kinney had met Alex Lultschik while working at Cold Metal's strip mill in Hamilton, Ontario, Canada. He'd recognized Lultschik's skillfulness immediately, and when Blair bought an oscillator in 2003—a machine used in the finishing process of certain grades of strip— Kinney hired Lultschik on a contract basis to get it up and running. To the unacquainted eye, the oscillator looks like an old, clunky machine, but with Lultschik's programming, it has become a finely tuned computer that produces the heaviest gauges of strip steel at a consistently high quality.

In 2014, Lultschik was brought back to computerize the operation of Blair's smaller mill, "Little Tom." The 2-stand, 4-high mill named in honor of Tom Blair was acquired in 1982. In its original state, the mill had a single function. That the mill was not more productive was a source of disappointment and frustration for Tom Blair. Kinney knew this, and with Blair metallurgist Gordon Wilber, he made a plan to refurbish the mill over time. It was a gesture of respect for Tom Blair that would also increase the mill's production.

Like any major change, the computerization of the mills created moments of friction between the old way and the new. When Little Tom was computerized, Mill Operator John Jopek had been at Blair for nearly twenty years. Prior to that he had worked at Elliott Brothers Steel—the same steelmaking Elliotts who had been partners with George Blair, Sr., in the early 1900s. Though Lultschik's methods could become tedious at times, Jopek's years of experience operating the mill allowed him to notice and appreciate the ways in which the computer could make the mill work perfectly—more perfectly than manual adjustments ever could. Jopek observed how the rolls lost contact at the end of a pass, which produced "heavy ends" that had to be sheared off as scrap. He asked if Lultschik could adjust the rolls to avoid the scrap ends. Indeed, Lultschik was able to program the mill's computer to reduce the roll pressure—a perfect solution toward making a better product.

Today, steelmaking is not the inevitably perilous, physically demanding work it was when Thomas Shoenberger Blair was experimenting with his direct process in the 1870s, nor does it require the same amount and type of manpower it did in the 1970s. Advancements in the technology of mills and plant equipment have helped increase safety, efficiency, and quality throughout the industry. Even with these advancements, good steelmaking sense is still a welcome skill at Blair. To Bruce Kinney, producing steel is a little art and a little science. Kinney notes that some maintenance specialists can listen to equipment and know something is wrong before they use technical diagnostics. He imagines that Tucker Nolan, George Blair, Jr., and others probably had that gift, too, from decades of experience working with the mill equipment.

Despite sophisticated technologies throughout, the Blair plant retains a bit of that old-school flavor. There is the presence of "Old Tucker," the oldest, smallest rolling mill on the premises, probably installed a short time after the fire in October 1930. In the shipping room are iron-wheeled carts that likely predated the fire. The brown door and archway that serve as the main entrance for mill employees are also symbols of the Blair of old and the way its heritage endures.

After Bruce Kinney took over on August 1, 1999, Tom Blair stayed at the company for two more months. He was pleased with his hire, and as much as he wanted to be a resource for Kinney, he also wanted to stay out of the way and let Kinney begin to execute his vision. Tom Blair left at the end of September, and though he remained chairman of the board, for the first time in fifty years he did not have an office in the little white house on Butler Avenue. He and Phyllis began to spend most of their time at their home in Florida but returned to New Castle regularly for board meetings.

The four years between that fateful lunch meeting at La Dolce Vita and Tom Blair's death in 2003 remain frozen in Bruce Kinney's mind. Kinney knew he was taking over for an extraordinary businessman and "an exemplary human." There was much more he had hoped to learn from Tom Blair, more wisdom to absorb, more stories and memories to receive and preserve. After their initial meeting, Kinney couldn't shake the feeling that it had been like talking to an older version of himself. Some years later, Tom's brother Dike Blair told Kinney that Tom had said that the conversation with Kinney had felt like talking to a younger version of himself. In Blair Strip Steel, Kinney found a place that aligned with his business philosophy, and in Bruce Kinney, Tom Blair found someone who would respectfully, intelligently, and prudently carry on the legacy of Blair Strip Steel and create the future he dared hope for it.

As it happens, it wasn't Bruce Kinney's dream to run a steel company or any company at all. When the opportunity at "Company X" came around, the forty-two-year-old husband and father wanted to take care of his family as well as he could and not waste the opportunities he was fortunate to have. When Tom Blair gave him the chance to keep a good company going, Kinney accepted it with humility. He felt his job was to preserve the best of what the Blairs had built, and down the road, pass on a version of the company in better shape than when he'd received it. By any measure, Bruce Kinney accomplished what he intended to do.

Just as Tom Blair knew when to look for the next bearer of the Blair legacy, so Bruce Kinney and the company's board of directors were able to recognize who would be the right person to lead Blair into its next era. In February 2019, chief financial officer Scott McDowell was named president of Blair Strip Steel.

As of the writing of this chapter of the Blair story, Bruce Kinney remains at Blair as the chief executive officer and chairman of the board of directors. At some point in the years to come, when Kinney is no longer making day-to-day decisions for Blair's future, he will write the next chapter of his own story, ready to see what the rest of the journey holds.

VP Operations John Avau (l) congratulates Bud Burns (r) for 34 years of service at the 2009 Blair Christmas celebration as General Manager Kevin Barren looks on. *Blair Strip Steel Company*

Holiday hams await distribution to all retirees and employees at the annual Christmas celebration. *Blair Strip Steel Company*

Scott McDowell and Beth Lysinger in 2009 *Blair Strip Steel Company*

Exterior view of BelleFlex Technologies in Ford City, PA. The company occupies two historic brick buildings that were in 1883 the original home of the Pittsburgh Plate Glass Company. *Blair Strip Steel Company*

BelleFlex personnel in 2014: (l to r) Jake Shafer, Engineer; Brad Astolos, Engineer; Bill Campbell, Chief Engineer; Frank Ballina, General Manager; Michele Males, Sales; Bill Barthlow, Assistant Manager; Chris Ziegler, Quality Control; Todd Cress, Operations; Dan Emanuele, Corporate Quality Director *Blair Strip Steel Company*

Long-time Blair employee Beth Lysinger holds a certificate confirming that she successfully climbed Mount Killamanjaro in June 2008. After a 37-year career at Blair, Lysinger retired in March 2020. *Blair Strip Steel Company*

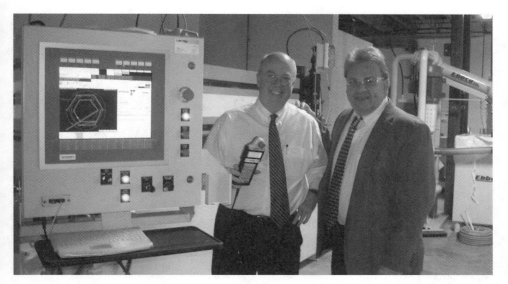

President & CEO Bruce Kinney with General Manager Frank Ballina at the opening of
BelleFlex Technologies in 2009 *Blair Strip Steel Company*

Turn Foreman Brian Holland inspects Big George in 2012. *Blair Strip Steel Company*

Blair General Foreman Pat Schooley hands a Christmas ham to retired Anneal Operator Ron Makarevich as Mike Monico (right) looks on. *Blair Strip Steel Company*

Bruce Kinney and BelleFlex Business Manager Bonnie DeAngeles having a laugh at BelleFlex Technologies in 2018 *Blair Strip Steel Company*

Slitting Foreman John Firmi (left) watches Joe Tomei crop the band on an incoming coil in 2012. *Blair Strip Steel Company*

When Hadden Blair joined the board of directors in 2003, he represented the fourth generation of Blairs to lead Blair Strip Steel and the eighth generation to contribute to the iron and steel industry of Pennsylvania.

Blair receiving the Supplier of the Year award from Precision Resource in 2018.
Pictured from left are Dave Fletcher, Mike Monico, Dan Harden, Jeff Murray, Dave Hogue, Dean Johnson, Tim Cwynar, Corey Beck, Dan Emanuele, Paul Johngrass, Larry Plummer, Karen Zubyk, Pat Schooley, Gary Campbell, The Unknown Workman, Mark Majors, Paul Eagle of Precision Resource, Steve Shipman, Marty Post, Zack Clouse, Jake Schooley, Chris Shevitz, John Moroco, Andy Dugan, Ken Hill, Donny Golba, Eric Ferringer, Matt Bruno, Bruce Kinney, Joe Surgenavic, Sam Flora, Tommy Villani, Ryan Sherwood, Kaveh Vafaei of Precision Resource, Bill Harvey, Albert Forletta, Ed Sheridan, Kevin Barren, Paul Graham, Darrell Montgomery, Dominic Sikora, Scott Kay, Scott McDowell, Dave Pastore, Mary Schell, John Bartko, Mary Pat Peretti, John Firmi, and Carole Sheen
Blair Strip Steel Company

CHAPTER 10

MEETING THE FUTURE: BELLEFLEX TECHNOLOGIES

We are continually faced by great opportunities brilliantly
disguised as insoluble problems.
>   —Lee Iacocca, American engineer
>   and auto executive (1924–2019)

I n the years immediately following World War II, young Tom Blair,
then an editor at *The Iron Age* magazine in New York City, and his
father, George, president of Blair Strip Steel, talked with each other
about the steel industry and what new challenges the company might
face. They were aware that Marshall Plan funds were being poured into
Germany and Japan to help rebuild the countries' steel manufacturing
infrastructure, which had been all but obliterated during the war. One of
George's close steelmaking colleagues in Pittsburgh was himself moving
to Japan for the opportunities he saw in the construction of a new,
completely modern steel industry. George speculated that it wouldn't be
long before a new steel producer abroad would begin competing with
producers in the US market. His speculation, would, of course, prove
to be correct when Japan's steel production soared during the 1950s and
'60s and dominated the global steel market until the rise of China's state-
owned steel industry in the 1990s.

During those discussions in the mid-1940s, father and son considered
how the company might expand into other markets in order to balance
their heavy dependence on the automotive industry. They agreed that the
company needed to stretch and explore but also stay small and avoid any
large capital risk. In essence, Blair needed an "outrigger" to balance the
steel operations. Above all else, they agreed, the timing for such a move
had to be right.

When Bruce Kinney joined Blair in 1999, he and Tom Blair resumed
those discussions. Not long into his tenure, Kinney imagined what other

technologies the company could explore to both expand beyond the automotive market and strategically create new ventures. Kinney shared his ideas with Tom Blair, and though he had Blair's support, Kinney knew it wasn't the right time for the company to make that kind of move. By then, the mill was more than seventy-five years old, and it was necessary to fix up, clean up, and modernize its operations before creating something new.

The right time came just a few years later. In 2009, as the Great Recession was coming to an end, Kinney and then-chief financial officer Scott McDowell launched BelleFlex Technologies as a wholly owned subsidiary of Blair Strip Steel to serve as both an outrigger for the steel business and a business incubator. The company's dual strategy is reflected in its name: "Belle" refers to the production of engineered Belleville disc springs and "flex" to the range of development projects meant to expand Blair's scope into components, systems, and materials other than steel. Fittingly, BelleFlex is headquartered in Ford City, Pennsylvania, just a mile down the Allegheny River from the birthplace of iron and steel innovator Thomas Shoenberger Blair, in two historic brick buildings that were in 1883 the original home of the Pittsburgh Plate Glass Company.

Kinney's strategy was to develop a core technology centered on engineered Belleville disc springs. The name "Belleville" is attributed to the French inventor Julien Belleville, who lived from 1823 until 1896, making him a contemporary of Thomas Shoenberger Blair (1825–1898). In 1867, the same year Blair and Carnegie's American Steeled Rail Company shipped samples of their new product to the Pennsylvania Railroad, Belleville patented a design that included the concept of a coned washer-like steel disc that functioned as a spring. The simple yet elegant design of Belleville disc springs makes them extraordinarily versatile, and when combined appropriately, the springs can support extremely heavy loads in a small installation space for a long time. But BelleFlex wouldn't just manufacture standard Belleville disc springs; Blair's new outrigger would engineer specialized Belleville disc springs to meet the demanding specifications of challenging industrial applications. In this way, BelleFlex would become a provider of "beautiful" (in French, *belle*) solutions to difficult problems.

Kinney and McDowell recognized an opportunity to access non-automotive markets, like the oil and gas industry that was quickly growing in Western Pennsylvania, as well as build a customer base across the globe. In order to make the new dream a reality, they hired Belleville spring industry veteran (and retired Major League Baseball umpire) Frank Ballina. They positioned BelleFlex precision spring components, assemblies, and systems as solutions to extraordinary engineering problems, especially those created by extreme heat or cold, very heavy loads, severe environmental conditions, and safety-critical or mission-critical applications.

Under Ballina's leadership and expertise, BelleFlex got to work engineering custom disc springs for a variety of applications, including essential components in downhole drilling tools, engine mounts for railroad locomotives, and supports for the enormous ladles that move molten steel through the air in steel mills. In time, the company developed critical actuators to operate reliably and precisely in deepwater drilling environments of the North Sea and South China Sea. For the National Oceanic and Atmospheric Administration (NOAA), BelleFlex produced "tsunameters"—devices that provide early detection of tsunamis— that operate on the floor of the Pacific Ocean and around the Pacific Rim. At the zenith of technically critical applications, BelleFlex Technologies produced critical safety components for the new docking system of the International Space Station (ISS). The initial docking adapter with the new BelleFlex spring system was aboard an unmanned SpaceX rocket in June of 2015 when the rocket exploded just after takeoff. However, subsequent spacecraft were successful in bringing three new docking systems to the ISS over the next two years. Now every spacecraft that visits the ISS carries the BelleFlex spring system on board.

While the BelleFlex business model is powered by disc spring technology, the company continues to develop non-metallic materials and components as well. The idea for a new product often comes when Senior Engineer Bill Campbell and his team of mechanical engineers look through a problem-solving lens, identifying challenges that a bit of creative yet sound engineering could solve. To address the problem of frequent and costly oil changes in diesel- and gasoline-powered engines and off-road and mass transit vehicles, BelleFlex is perfecting a two-stage purification system to filter, dehydrate, and recycle engine or hydraulic oil instead of replacing it. The same technology has been scaled for use in larger industrial applications like hydraulic systems, generators, and wind turbines, and as of the publication of this book, a mobile version of the system will be tested at Marietta College's Department of Petroleum Engineering.

The BelleFlex engineering team saw similar problems and potential solutions with structural panels, cargo pallets, and numerous other applications. They designed a high-strength composite panel and tested it extensively, finding that it withstood horizontal impact much better than an all-aluminum panel. They took a similar approach with the wooden cargo decks in commercial truck beds. Those wood panels were, by nature, heavy and susceptible to rot from trapped moisture, so BelleFlex designed and produced a stronger, lighter, waterproof version using modern composite materials called "CorePlate" that will have a wide range of commercial applications.

While the materials BelleFlex develops and the computer-automated machinery it uses are considered the height of modern technology, the engineering concepts that underpin certain products have been around for millennia. On a trip to Venice, Italy, Bruce Kinney happened to glimpse the engineering solution that keeps the whole city from sinking into the Venetian Lagoon. In an open construction site, he saw what looked like a foundation made from wooden pilings. Indeed, he learned, the city of Venice was constructed upon a bed of cut alder trunks. These trees had been farmed especially for this purpose, then cut to about sixty feet long and driven into the muddy floor of the Adriatic Sea. Though wood might seem like a temporary solution given its susceptibility to moisture damage, the mineral-rich water actually petrified the wood, adding even greater strength to the foundation. The Venetians were said to have borrowed this engineering idea from the ancient Egyptians, who used bundles of reeds in many of their engineering solutions, including building boats. Papyrus reeds were plentiful and accessible, and when bound tightly together, they created a strong, durable building material. As early as 2600 BC, the Egyptians replicated the strength of the reed bundles in stone columns, which the Greeks and Romans would use as architectural compression members to support heavy stone structures for centuries to follow. Although the materials have changed over time, the design concepts remained the same.

After a few years, it became clear to Kinney that the business incubator half of the BelleFlex business model was working. The company's opportunities in specialty polymer composites were increasing. Under the composite engineering expertise of Craig Lawson and Stephen Mansfield, BelleFlex was producing very high-quality fiberglass and carbon fiber pultrusions. The products were meeting the specifications for more and more specialty applications, including composite materials with a high strength-to-weight ratio, hybrid resin systems, ultraviolet stability, low thermal conductivity, fire resistance, and custom woven or stitched materials. They were gaining customers in the wind and solar energy industries, construction, architectural façade, and transportation. It was time again for Kinney, McDowell, and their colleagues to let the business stretch and expand, albeit judiciously. At the end of 2017, PulFlex Technologies was created as a subsidiary of BelleFlex, and Lawson and Mansfield began operations immediately in a space adjacent to BelleFlex in Ford City. In summer 2018, Ben Kessing was brought into the Blair fold to serve as general manager of BelleFlex and PulFlex. Like Bruce Kinney when he was hired to lead Blair Strip Steel, Kessing was relatively young in age when he arrived at BelleFlex but mature in the vision he held for Blair's modern materials and components group.

Like its parent company, BelleFlex Technologies is not in the business of making "plain vanilla." Instead, it aims to be the most knowledgeable, specialized producer in the engineered spring industry. Likewise, PulFlex has positioned itself as a small producer of high-quality composites using the process of pultrusion, which is considered a niche craft in the larger composite industry. As with the strip steel arm of the business, BelleFlex's market advantage is having the engineering expertise and mechanical capacity to take on custom orders—many with steep specifications—and deliver a high-quality product.

For Kinney, one of the goals of having an outrigger business like BelleFlex was the chance for Blair to participate in the global marketplace. To date, BelleFlex has served customers in more than forty countries. Nonetheless, it identifies as a thoroughly American enterprise with Pennsylvania craftsmanship underpinning the success of its products.

Woven into the fabric of BelleFlex, too, is the history and culture of the Blair family. Alive in the business is the legacy of Thomas Shoenberger Blair, who was not content to rely on the technologies of the present moment or rest on his own or his company's proverbial laurels. He thrived on solving problems, especially those problems in manufacturing—and in society— that created unnecessary costs for everyone involved, from customers to owners to laborers.

BelleFlex also bears the mark of Tom Blair. Though the project came to fruition after his lifetime, he was nonetheless involved in its strategic framework. Given Tom Blair's creative engineering mind, Kinney knows his predecessor would have been fascinated by the work being done at the company today and proud of the forward-thinking ethos it was founded upon.

CHAPTER 11

As If People Mattered: The Culture of Blair Strip Steel

Today we honor our retirees—we stand on your broad
shoulders, just as we all stand with more than two centuries
of good, hard-working Blair men and women.
—Bruce Kinney, President and CEO
of Blair Strip Steel, December 2015

You won't find many people who *used to* work at Blair Strip Steel. Most Blair employees are hired, stay for a decade or two or three, and then retire, having spent the greater part of their careers at the company. When Jack Allen started at Blair in the early 1960s, thirty mill employees had been there for more than thirty years. As Jim Stillwagon put it, "In my twenty-five years here, I can count the number of quits in the mill on one hand and have fingers left." Tucker Nolan was on the payroll at Blair for an astounding seventy-three years, beginning with his first job as a Push-n-Puller until his death in 2001 at the age of ninety-six while he was still a member of the board of directors. Given these epic tenures, it's no wonder that for the first fifteen years he worked at Blair, current president Scott McDowell was considered "the new guy."

Why, throughout the company's long history, have so many employees chosen to spend most of their lives at Blair? According to the employees themselves, the reasons are many: for the fair pay and excellent benefits; for the way workers and retirees are treated with respect; for the get-it-done spirit that infuses every department and role in the company; for the bond Blair employees forge with each other; for the chance to have a good life outside of work.

Corporate executives at much larger companies spend hundreds of hours and millions of dollars on team building and talent retention, but the culture of loyalty at Blair appears not to be the result of a calculated strategy or initiative. It is baked into the bones of the place. Since its founding, and beginning with George Blair, Jr., the leaders of Blair Strip Steel have run the company as if the employees matter—a philosophy that no paycheck, bonus schedule, or amount of vacation time can quite replace.

Time and again, current Blair employees and retirees talk about *wearing many hats* and *doing what needs to be done*. In the words of Jack Allen, "Everyone does everything at Blair." The spirit of pitching in transcends position or hierarchy. Long-time employees and managers are just as committed to doing what needs to be done as the newest employee who is trying to prove himself or herself—perhaps even more so. When talking about this phenomenon, one Blair employee remarked, "The other day, I saw John hauling out the recycling. He's the vice president of manufacturing! That's not his job, but it needed to be done, so he did it." Warren Enscoe, now retired from the mill, pitches in to help care for the grounds of the company. Occasionally, he'll use his brush hog to clear out overgrowth not because he has to or because he is paid to do the work, but because it "just needs to be done."

Without prompting, Blair employees and retirees talk about the camaraderie within the company. In the same spirit as *doing what needs to be done*, coworkers tend to help each other and watch each other's backs instead of being concerned only with their own. Men who worked in the mill for decades tell stories about trading shifts so a fellow worker could go duck hunting or attend an important family event. Others remember volunteering to stay two hours past the end of the afternoon shift to make sure a big contract with a key customer would be completed on time.

Get him going and every guy who worked in the mill has a story about the people he worked with and the good times they had. In the days of Tom Blair and mill superintendent Tucker Nolan, the work environment was a lot looser compared with steel mills today. Horseplay was a given. Soaking a poor, unsuspecting soul with a bucket of cold water or greasing the handles of a wheelbarrow were everyday gags. One incident in the 1970s involved a bottle rocket and a very close call. Tucker had a habit of walking around the plant with his head down, and the rocket, which was launched out of a pipe, whizzed past his ear. Surely the "Silver Fox" heard it—or at least felt it—but he never directly disciplined the guilty parties for it. There seemed to be an understanding between the old-school superintendent and his mill men: as long as the work got done and nobody got hurt, the rest was not his concern. Says one retiree, "In those days, sometimes scrap would pile up like bales of Slinky. Once, part of it hooked onto a guy's lunch bucket and dragged it into the scrap machine. He left a note for Tucker that read, 'You owe me one lunch bucket and a ham sandwich.'" With every story about the good times, the reprise is, "We had our fun but got our work done."

The guys who joked together also took their lumps together. Blair retiree Richie Carbone described the time some of his fellow mill workers cut out of their shift a few minutes early. Tucker knew Richie wasn't one of the offenders, but Tucker docked him anyway. On one hand, Richie was part of the team, so he was held responsible; on the other hand, Tucker wanted to see if Richie would stay loyal to his guys. Though it might have had repercussions for his own production bonus, Richie didn't complain to Tucker, but he also made sure his guys didn't do it again.

Legendary bales of scrap notwithstanding, maintenance and cleanliness have always been closely held values in the Blair mill. Every summer there is a planned shutdown to tackle deep cleaning and address any concerns with equipment that, if properly managed, may prevent unplanned work stoppages during the year. Until the early 1980s, about twenty mill employees would work on replacing sections of worn-out flooring during the summer shutdown. Humidity made the creosote blocks expand and buckle. These "blow-ups" were no longer a problem after the blocks were replaced with composite flooring. Doing even dirtier work than usual in the heat of summer wasn't anyone's idea of a good time, but the guys who had floor repair duty made the most of it, and at the end of the second week, they celebrated their efforts with cold beers.

Socializing has always been bedrock to the company's culture. That people who are paid to work together also want to spend time with each other outside of work is a testament to the bond among Blair employees. For decades, the mill men would finish their Saturday morning shift and go straight to Troggio's for a meal. After being overwhelmed a few times by the flood of workers fresh off the job, the restaurant staff was prepared for the shift change and had food plated and ready to serve when the hungry crowd burst through the doors. The same was true on paydays. Troggio's would call to see when they guys were getting their checks so the bar would be fully stocked and ready for the tidal wave of thirsty men newly flush with cash. Likewise, the main office staff was fond of holding "band practice" on Friday after work—tongue-in-cheek code for going out for drinks.

Though there was no actual company band, Blair did have a company baseball team. At least four years before an NFL franchise by the same name hit Pittsburgh, the Steelers of Blair Strip Steel were roughing up the competition in New Castle. "Teams desiring games with a first class ball club can arrange them calling 5209," declared the write-up in the *New Castle News* on June 5, 1929. "Any team in the city and county will be met by the Steelers." A team called Rhodes Mission answered the call for competition and was defeated by the Steelers 7-2. Leading the effort was a pitcher by the name of Turco who "allowed but four hits."

During Tom Blair's tenure, the company had ties to another baseball team: the Pittsburgh Pirates. Minority owner and vice president of the ball club, Thomas Phillips Johnson, was a long-standing member of the Blair Strip Steel board of directors. Tom Johnson was born and raised in New Castle and co-founded Kirkpatrick & Lockhart, once the largest law firm in Pittsburgh. He became an owner of the Pirates organization and Forbes Field in 1946. He was dedicated to the team and was well liked among the ballplayers and staff. During his involvement, he attended 55 consecutive Pirates openers and went to almost every home game, at which he always kept score. As both a business associate and a friend of Tom Blair, Tom Johnson served on the board of Blair Strip Steel for forty-five years. Powerful businessman though he was, Tom Johnson is often described as modest and approachable, much like Tom Blair. One Blair board member said he could "sit down and talk to Mr. Johnson like he was a next-door neighbor."

Not long after Tom Johnson acquired part-ownership of the Pirates, other individuals including the actor Bing Crosby became involved. Through his connection to Tom Johnson, Tom Blair came to know Bing Crosby and other Hollywood celebrities. Though their fame did not dazzle Tom Blair, now and then he would leverage his notable connections when entertaining customers on the West Coast. One customer, who was known as a quiet, non-social type, looked forward to Mr. Blair's sales calls because the steel supplier from Pennsylvania would introduce him to his famous friends. The customer once found himself in a limousine with Tom Blair, Bing Crosby, actor Jimmy Stewart, and another strip steel manufacturer whose name was Robert Wagner, Sr.—the father of the actor Robert Wagner—on their way to one of Crosby's ranches. For Tom Blair, the appeal was never the brush with stardom or fodder for name-dropping, though he admitted the group had some fun. Ultimately, the goal was to keep his customers happy, which kept the orders coming in and the business going.

It was important to Tom Blair that his employees felt appreciated and had some fun, too. Profits from the vending machines in the mill went toward funding an amusement park outing for all mill employees. Every summer for years the company held a picnic for employees and their families at Cascade Park in New Castle. In August 2013, Blair threw a birthday party to mark ninety years since the company's founding in 1923. Blair employees and their families, as well as all 156 living retirees, the board of directors, and several members of the Blair family gathered in SNPJ, Pennsylvania, to enjoy food, drinks, and games. Said one attendee, "It didn't matter what position you had—laborer, board member, manager—everyone was out there in shorts and t-shirts playing cornhole and having a good time." Partygoers had the chance to reminisce in a tent lined with photographs from the company's ninety-year history. At the end of the day, everyone went home with Blair-branded party favors.

Of all the Blair traditions, arguably the most cherished and meaningful continues to be the annual Christmas Cash celebration. Once upon a time it was a wild affair with whiskey and cigars, but it has since become a moment of genuine appreciation that echoes the generosity of George Blair, Jr., and his managers during the depths of the Great Depression. A few mornings before Christmas, all Blair retirees are invited back to the mill for coffee and doughnuts. Current employees stop work and join the retirees as the president says a few words about the previous year, including a recap of challenges the company faced and goals it reached. And then, in order of seniority, each employee is called up individually to receive his or her production bonus. If it's a milestone year for someone—say ten years on the job, or twenty, or twenty-five, or thirty—the employee's supervisor or a colleague will offer a few words of praise. One year, general foreman Pat Schooley recognized a young man who had reached twenty years in the mill, though he looked like he couldn't have been older than forty. Schooley called the young man "a diamond in the rough" and said he "sounded like a telemarketer" on the phone, which got a laugh from the crowd.

As each employee accepts his or her check, Blair managers offer handshakes and sincere thanks for a year of good work. All attendees, including retirees, are given a ham or turkey to take home and enjoy with their families. To outsiders, this may seem like a minor gesture, especially compared with bonus pay; however, the extra gift is a tangible symbol of the way Blair takes care of its people and treats them as if they matter—even after they have retired from the company. Many retirees look forward to the Christmas gathering because it's a chance to catch up with each other. They enjoy seeing their buddies who are still working at the mill and relish the chance to talk about old times. The greatest part of the experience, which goes largely unspoken, is the feeling that they haven't been forgotten. Blair is the place it is today thanks to their efforts, and though times change and bodies aren't as young and invincible as they used to be, their years of dedication are recognized and appreciated. They are still part of the family.

———————

Attn: Scott A. McDowell and Bruce Kinney
Re: Joseph A. Hritz
From: Edna Hritz

When I met Joseph in 1960, he was laid off from Blair Strip Steel. He told me he hated signing up for unemployment because he felt others were in more need. Early in 1961, Joseph suffered a massive stroke at 29 years old. He could not walk, talk, or see. After hospitalization, recuperation, and tender loving care, he was called back to work. We married on November 3, 1962.

In the first four to five years of our marriage he worked six to seven days a week. Joe was employed in the Shipping Department. The Blairs gave him the name "Shoulders," because of his expertise loading and unloading the trucks. The summer picnics were a big family affair. Many prizes of value were won by the workmen and families. At Thanksgiving, we were given turkeys, and at Christmas a ham or turkey—employees' choice. Those came in handy for those of us raising families, buying our homes, etc.

At Christmastime [in 1976], Joe was to replace Mr. John Polenick as boss of the Shipping Department. John was going to retire. (John's brother, Mike, also worked at Blair.) Just prior to starting our summer vacation, Joe was experiencing a little problem with his health. Unfortunately, and to the shock of many, he had a massive heart attack and died on July 14, 1976. It was devastating to the Blairs, me, and my family. Our sons were 12, 10, and 7 years old at the time.

When I mention that Joe had worked at Blair Strip, I hear nothing but great comments from others. Over the years, I've been blessed by what I have received from Blair Strip Steel. The extra monies enabled me to help raise my boys. Joe would be extremely proud of their accomplishments, their wives, and our grandchildren.

June 2014

Dear Friends at Blair Strip Steel:

My wife, Pearl, our family, and I are so proud to have been part of Blair Strip Steel for 47 years. We have so many blessings and memories. I am so thankful for all my friends and everyone who touched my life.

Back in March of 1951, my brother-in-law, Robert Roush, who was employed at Blair, had some papers that needed to be signed. I went with him and he took me in the mill. I was 18 years old and married and was working at a dairy in Enon Valley. A man came up to me and asked if I was looking for work. I said no. My brother-in-law said, "Do you know who he is?" I said no! He said, "That was Tucker Nolan, Superintendent of the mill." Pretty soon, Mr. Nolan asked me if I was sure I didn't want a job. I changed my answer and was glad he wanted me. He took me in the office and said I could start in a week: April 1, 1951, on the midnight turn.

I gave my notice at my job and our family moved back up to New Castle. That was the best day that could ever have happened to our family. We didn't have a car or even a television. I loved my job and spent so many years learning and sharing my life with Tucker Nolan, Glenn Turner, and all the wonderful men at Blair. Blair took care of my family.

. . . May you continue to bless many other young families to find the love and help they need.

James D. Phillips
New Castle, PA

Like James "Big Daddy" Phillips, many retirees express how grateful they are for their career at Blair, saying that Blair allowed them to provide for their loved ones and create a better life for them. Even after Joseph Hritz died, the company helped Edna Hritz care for her sons, a gesture that made a significant impact on the family's well-being.

Blair employees often shared "the best-kept secret" that was working at Blair with their family members. Just as Jimmy Phillips had tagged along on an errand to the mill with his brother-in-law and came back with a job, many lifelong Blair employees ended up at the company because a relative worked there and spoke highly of the place. Similarly, Joseph Hritz's brother-in-law, Albert "Bookie" Book worked at Blair for twenty-three years, and Albert's brother, Clair Book, worked in the mill, too. In December 2015, the Enscoe family realized there had been seven family members who worked at Blair in some capacity—Dick, Carl, Bob, Bill, Warren, Warren Jr., and Rob—and there had been at least one Enscoe at Blair in all the preceding forty-five years. Hired in 2008, Rob Enscoe was set to have a long, successful career at Blair, but his life was cut short in 2014 after sustaining a lethal bee sting while playing outside with his young family. In his brief time at Blair, Rob carried on the strong Enscoe tradition of loyalty and dedication to work and family.

Time and again, retirees say they felt an innate sense of security at Blair. Throughout their careers they believed they would be treated fairly and didn't worry that the company would suddenly go out of business one day because of reckless management or corporate downsizing. Job security and good pay can inspire loyalty, but so does caring about an employee's life outside of work. There are countless stories about how Blair has supported employees' families beyond providing a reliable paycheck. One such story is about a mill employee who quit work to care for his terminally ill wife and had a job waiting for him back at Blair after she passed away.

A similar story involves Tucker Nolan. Even if his demeanor was about as soft as the heavy-gauge strip that rolled out of the mill, Tucker saw his men as the people they were, not just as employees. One Blair retiree, Norman Black, had been working at Blair for only three months when his wife became very ill and needed to go to the Cleveland Clinic for specialized care. When Norman told Tucker that he would be missing work in the coming weeks so he could take his wife to Cleveland, Tucker offered to tap one of his contacts at the Clinic to get the Blacks an appointment even sooner. He also offered to cover the family's hotel expenses. Norman declined both offers, but he was deeply touched that his boss would be so generous, especially to an employee Tucker had known for such a short time.

Tucker Nolan's devotion to Blair employees and their families extends to people he would never meet during his lifetime. Each year, the Thomas E. Nolan Educational Assistance Program awards grants to all Blair employees' children who are pursuing post-high school degrees. With every college course completed thanks to that funding, the impact of Tucker Nolan's generosity continues.

As both Tom Blair's secretary and a staff person who mastered just about every task in the main office, Karen Ippolito had a long and fulfilling career at Blair. Fewer than two years after being hired, Karen got married and had her first child. She left work when her son was born but returned shortly after his first birthday. She left again a few years later to raise her other children and came back six years later to continue typing flawless letters in record time and to help with anything and everything that needed to be done. In telling her story, Karen expressed how deeply grateful she was to Mr. Blair for allowing her to fulfill her responsibilities as a wife and mother and know that she would have a job when she was able to return. For Tom Blair's part, he knew he had an excellent employee in Karen Ippolito, and he chose to value her needs not because it was federally mandated but because both the company and Karen would benefit.

From the beginning, taking care of its people has been part of "the Blair way." Since the company's founding, Joe and Vera Punio had rented a house on the property next door to Blair Strip Steel. Mrs. Punio cleaned Blair's main office, and Joe, who was seldom seen without his wheelbarrow, cared for the company grounds. In the 1930s and '40s, it was not uncommon to see president George Blair and Joe Punio sitting together under a shade tree on a bright summer day, enjoying a break and smoking Bull Durham tobacco. The Punios were such valued members of the Blair Strip Steel family that when Joe died, Tom Blair bought the adjacent property to ensure that Mrs. Punio could remain living in her house as long as she wanted.

Throughout the company's history, Blair's board of directors has always been small and focused, but it has played a crucial role in preserving the best aspects of the Blair way of doing business. In 2020, the board includes Hadden Blair, son of Tom Blair; former mill superintendent Glenn Turner; current president Scott McDowell; and CEO Bruce Kinney. Two more directors round out the group, bringing experience and insight from outside the arena of steelmaking. For decades, George Weingartner owned and operated a floral business in New Castle which included several retail shops and a garden center. He brought to the board a strong sense of entrepreneurship, as well as an understanding of the New Castle community. He also brought a long-held respect for the Blair family and Blair Strip Steel. His father, Robert A. Weingartner, had served on the Blair board of directors for many years and made it clear that anything having to do with Blair was "top drawer." What's more, the Weingartners could trace their connection to Blair all the way back to the beginning: George's grandfather, George T. Weingartner, was a founding partner in the company. When George D. Blair, Sr., began issuing stock for his new enterprise, George T. Weingartner bought certificate no. 0006.

Brenda K. McBride, long-time partner at the law firm McBride & McBride in Grove City, Pennsylvania, brought much-needed legal expertise to the Blair board of directors in 2004. Her father, Milford "Miff" McBride, a well-known lawyer in the New Castle/Grove City area, had been a golfing buddy and close confidant of Tom Blair. "We lost a lot of golf balls together," Tom Blair once said about his friend, Miff. It was also Miff McBride who introduced Tom Blair to Paul Brown. The McBrides and Blairs socialized often, and even as a young person, Brenda McBride recognized the qualities that made Tom Blair so respected and admired in his company: "He was the essence of a gentleman. He always listened. He was never looking over your shoulder for someone more important. You were it."

As much as Bruce Kinney learned from Tom Blair during the short time he knew him, Kinney also gained much from his relationship with Tom's brother, Dike Blair. Dike's presence on the Blair Strip Steel board of directors was important to Kinney. At the time of Tom's death in 2003, Dike had been on the board for almost fifty-five years and was a representative voice from the Blair family. While most of the other board members were professionals from the steel, legal, and financial sectors, Dike had spent most of his adult life as the owner of a small independent bookstore. He brought a fresh perspective to the group, and Kinney enjoyed swapping stories and exploring ideas with him. It was a true loss for Kinney and the company when Dike Blair passed away in October 2009.

When Dike was still able to travel from Vermont to New Castle for Blair board meetings, the two discovered they shared an interest in the economist and philosopher E.F. Schumacher. Schumacher's book, *Small is Beautiful: Economics As If People Mattered*, had deeply influenced the thinking of both men. The phrase "small is beautiful" could very well be one of the unwritten credos of Blair Strip Steel. There was a time in the 1960s when Blair could have scaled up and dominated the strip industry, but Tom Blair opted for preservation over growth. By remaining small and privately held, Blair would retain advantages over its larger, publicly traded competitors.

For Blair, running the business "as if people mattered" has meant that the company does its best to balance equally the interests of its employees, customers, shareholders, and the community. Current president Scott McDowell and CEO Bruce Kinney believe in maintaining high "quality of work life"; they want Blair employees and consultants to be able to spend their days in an environment that promotes the development and use of their full abilities, as people and as members of a company.

In terms of employees, Blair is smaller than it was fifty years ago. Since 1999, about seventy or eighty people work at Blair at any given time, a number that includes the main office staff, salespeople, and mill workers. Blair's small size remains one of its most attractive qualities to potential employees. Several current Blair managers spent years moving from opportunity to opportunity at much larger steel companies, growing disillusioned by the instability of the organizations and ruthlessness of their work environments. Besides a healthier culture and enhanced job security, working at a smaller shop appealed to them because they wouldn't just be one of many, replaceable at any moment. When fewer people are doing the work, each person's impact is greater. So it is at Blair.

In the midst of the festivities at Blair's ninetieth birthday celebration, a long-time associate of the company gestured at the happy summer scene. "This is not a company picnic," he said. "This is a family picnic." Indeed, the gathering felt more like a reunion of long-lost relatives than people who, for a time, worked at the same place.

But Blair has that effect on people.

Anymore, it's difficult not to feel a surge of cynicism when a company—large or small—claims to value family and "a culture of cooperation." Corporatespeak is just that: talk. What Blair has that most companies don't is nearly a hundred years of proof that hiring the right employees and treating them well does pay—in productivity, in loyalty, and in living to see the long run.

Dozens of Blair employees and associates appear in the stories in this book, but hundreds more, who are not directly mentioned, played crucial roles in the success of Blair Strip Steel. The company would not have survived without their devotion and their pride in doing good work. They have made Blair a place where a person can make not just a living but also a life.

EPILOGUE

AN AMERICAN EVOLUTION

The narrative about the shrinking US steel industry is, by now, a familiar one. Indeed, the last forty years have been a tough time to be an American steelmaker, in large part due to increasing globalization. In 1985, the US and China were producing roughly the same amount of steel. Since then, the US steel industry has shrunk to about 88 million tonnes of capacity, and China's has grown more than tenfold, to 996 million tonnes of capacity (2019). By creating this enormous over-capacity, China has driven the price of their steel well below global prices and has enticed manufacturers to do business in China. Since 2000, US steelmakers have experienced more than 30 bankruptcies and have cut more than one third of all steel jobs, forcing the industry to reorganize and consolidate to survive. Household names that for generations stood as symbols of American steel manufacturing have become memories from a different time.

December 2023 will mark 100 years since the founding of Blair Strip Steel. As its history shows, Blair has not been immune to the economic pressures and threats that have put other companies out of business. So it's natural to wonder: Why has Blair survived when so many other steelmakers have not? In the face of adversity, two strategies have helped Blair live to see one hundred: be the right size and be willing to evolve.

Blair Strip Steel has always been a relatively small shop compared with most steel producers. At its largest, Blair employed not many more than 100 people. Today, Blair continues to be a small company by desire and by design. Under the leadership of Bruce Kinney, the company recommitted to taking a long-term view, focusing on sustaining the business and making measured progress instead of growing for the sake of growth. In this way, small is not only "beautiful" as Schumacher's philosophy suggests, but small is also smart. By staying agile, Blair is able to meet the needs of its customers and respond to industry challenges in a way that larger companies cannot.

But being small is not the point; being "right-sized" is. Kinney, McDowell, and the Blair leadership are committed to keeping Blair Strip Steel and BelleFlex sized appropriately for the specialty markets the companies serve. Blair and BelleFlex are more specialized than ever. They make products for demanding applications in small lots and at a high cost. No plain vanilla—just the best fudge ripple money can buy.

Just as important as being the right size has been Blair's willingness to evolve intelligently. Evolving has meant embracing change in the face of uncertainty—changing the company's product mix, changing its customer base, and changing how the established business can be balanced by new technologies. In essence, the Blair story is one of reinvention: from nails to rails in Thomas Shoenberger Blair's days managing the Shoenbergers' rolling mill; from iron to light gauge strip steel when George Blair partnered with the Elliott Brothers of New Castle; from light gauge to heavy gauge strip when Blair Strip Steel was established; from commodity steel to specialty steel, and then from steel products to industrial components and systems with the advent of BelleFlex and PulFlex.

It took remarkable vision and courage for the leaders of Blair to recognize when evolution was necessary and then to make it happen. But the Blair story is filled with remarkable leaders who had in them a pioneering spirit. They were up to the challenge of solving problems and going a way not yet traveled. The Blairs were people who stood in dense forestland at the base of a mountain and imagined a packhorse route to the other side; who laid a path where there wasn't one and did what needed to be done to make it happen; who used the gifts and opportunities they were given with generosity and humility; who dared to invent a new steelmaking process; who recognized when to brace against the storm and when to chart a different course. Each made personal sacrifices to keep a good thing going and showed what can happen when you bring together smart, talented, hard-working individuals and treat them like the valuable assets they are.

For many, Blair is a truly remarkable place. During the company's ninetieth birthday celebration, a board member felt a pang of wistfulness as he took in the happy scene. "You know, a Blair kind of place is going away," he said. "You don't find this kind of place anymore." Though Blair has survived by embracing change and by not clinging to the way things have always been done, there is value in looking back and remembering, in celebrating the spirit of a company and reflecting on what has made it successful for so long.

Years ago, long-time Blair board member Robert A. Weingartner explained to his son, current board member George Weingartner, what sets Blair apart. "In business," he said, "a lot of people do things the right way. A lot of people do things the wrong way. The Blair way is a cut above the right way." To many, "the Blair way" is about respect and fairness, profitability and humanity. It's about how a company truly can balance the interests of its employees, customers, shareholders, and the larger community, and still prosper. It's about having one hundred years of evidence that it is possible to get by in this swift and expanding world while maintaining that *how* one does business and *who* benefits from it matter just as much as a coil of steel, the value of a stock, the bottom line. These are the lights that will guide the Blair legacy for the next 100 years.

THE PEOPLE OF BLAIR STEEL

WILLIAM MCCORMICK

GEORGE MOORE

JOHN KOMARC

TOM JONES

JOHN NOGEE

WILLIAM GOULD

JOSEPH CROACH

DONALD GOLBA

CHRISTOPHER ZEIGLER

DANIEL HARDEN

ANGELO PACE

WALTER SONNTAG

LEONARD WISE

SCOTT KAY

JOSEPH HRITZ

RONALD GALLUCCI

VITTORIO MALIZIA

JOHN VINCEY

WILLIAM HENSELL

RAMESHWAR NARINE

RYAN SHERWOOD

WILLIAM HARVEY

LOUIS TODORA

RANDY GARTNER

JOHN KUKKOLA

DAVID PEARSON II

RUSSELL HARDSOCK

MARK MAJORS

LANCE HILL

THOMAS STOOPS

JAMES CRAWFORD

JACOB SLOSARCSIK

THOMAS HUNT

ANGELA BROCIOUS

ZACHARY CLOUSE

CARL GERMANSKI

CARLO ALBERTINI

DAVID DICKINSON

RICHARD BIGLEY

JEFFREY MCMURRAY

EDWARD PRESNAR

LEROY JONES

CONRAD KAPCEWICZ

MICHAEL SMETANA

MIKE LENHART

ANDREW POLENICK

LOUIS FERRARI

JOHNS MERLE

ANGELO CIALONE

DAVID GERMANSKI

SAM ANGELO

PAUL JORDAN

JAMES STILLWAGON

DEBRA YOUNG

GARY BUCHOWSKI

MICHAEL MONICO

RAYMOND HEINLE

GEORGE JONES

ERMIN SALLMEN

BERARDINO PIETRANGELI

ROYCE REICHEL

LEWIS PRESNAR

NICOLA EZZO

ROBERT WILSON, JR

HENRY ABRAMSKI

WILLIAM JOHNSON

KAREN IPPOLITO

WILLIAM SMITH

PAUL WHITE

LARRY PLUMMER

CHARLES WAGNER

JOSEPH LENHART

JOHN HUDAK

ANGELO VITTO

ALBERT CARAVELLA

JAMES PAVLINA

RONALD EDWARDS

RAYMOND MILLER

CHASE SCHELL

STUART BARTOSHEK

ANDY SHEVITZ

ERIK FERRINGER

AARON BENINCASE

MIKE POLENICK, JR

RICHARD WHITTAKER

JAMES WISE

QUITO CRESARI

LIVIO FEDRIZZI

CHRISTOPHER KRUPA

NORMAN MARTIN

DANNY SMOLNIK

STEPHEN KELLER

SAMUEL TIECHE

JOSEPH DONNELLY

ROBERT KEYS

ROBERT SCHAEFFER

JAMES BARRETT

DAVID PALUS

STANLEY NYCH

DAVID AIKEN

WILLIAM CUBELLIS

WILLIAM LYYTINEN

CLYDE VOGAN

RICHARD HERTHEL

ROBERT CHAMBERLAIN

RHONDA HEYDLE

CARL ENSCOE

WALTER MCCOLLUMS

TIMOTHY CWYNAR

SABRINA CAMPBELL

ANTHONY HORN

HOWARD YOHO

RICHARD HAMMERS

GEORGE WEINGARTNER

JAMES PERRY

GERALD LANE

NORMAN HOOVER

LESTER ALTMAN, JR

WILLIAM CHESLOCK

LARRY WIMER

GARY CAMPBELL

JOHN FORMATI

KEVIN BARREN

JEFFREY MURPHY

DAVID MYER

FRANK CALL

JOHN MYRTA

RICHARD INNOCENT

J. AUSTIN MURPHY

MERLE WOMER

JOHN AVAU

ROBERT JONES

FRED BRUCE

CAROLE SHEEN

THOMAS PLACHA

NICHOLAS LOVAGLIO

HARRY JERMAKOWICZ

VERONICA DEANGELIS

NYTODY BOZLINSKI

JEROME GENTILE

ANDREW DILORENZO

CHRISTOPHER WIRE

CHARLES KALICHUN

ROBERT ENSCOE

PHILIP MILLS

BRADLEY ASTOLOS

NORMAN BINTRIM

JUSTIN KOBIK

GINO GUIDUCCI

JOSEPH BOK

STEVE LENHART

STEVE KOPSKY

GLENN BABER

JOSEPH MILLS

ANDREW ZIDLOW

BRENDA MCBRIDE

CHARLES WARNECK

MICHAEL DADO

WILLIAM DONALDSON

RICHARD SWARTZ

JOSEPH SURGENAVIC

JOHN BLAIR

JAMES JANOVICK

HOWARD HOOVER

LENARD ANDERSON

HAROLD GLENN

FRANK VITTO

LARRY JONES, JR

MIKE POLENICK, SR

NICHOLAS SELEMON

JACOB SCHOOLEY

JOE GARCZYNSKI

ARTHUR MIELKE

ADAM NASAL

MATTHEW HARLAN

ROBERT GREAF

JULIA GILBOY

JOHN PETRO

NICHOLAS HOLMES

DAVID FLETCHER

PAUL JOHNGRASS

NANCY WILLIAMS

LELAND BROWN III

LYSLE NIMMO

ANTHONY NAKONECZNY

JOHN SMOLNIK

DANIEL SPAYDE

FELIX MALIZIA

MELVIN ANTHONY, JR

THOMAS BLAIR

JAMES HOBEL

VICTOR ECKLUND

EDWARD KELLEY

COREY BECK

JONAS DOSCH	JOHN WIDELKO
EMIL SMOLNIK	LEWIS PUHL
CESIDIO CAMILLO	THOMAS KELLY
RICHARD ENSCOE	NANCY ORRICO
STEPHEN BURICK	GEORGE T. WEINGARTNER
ROBERT HEINRICH	ROBERT MARTIN
WILLIAM DORAN	EMMETT BURNS
THOMAS JONES	JEFFREY FILER, JR
STEVEN MCCURDY	HARRY DIEHL
ALBERT BOOK	CODY CLEM
KENNETH HILL	CLAUDE DAVIS
MIKE FUGUS	QUENTIN FOX
KAREN ZUBYK	RICHARD PURSELL
JEFFREY KRAMER, JR	FRANK MYRTA
KIRK CURILLA	RONALD MAKAREVICH
VICTOR SABINO	ANGELO APICELLI
LEE BAILY	ALFRED VERZILLI
TONY DRAPKO	VICTOR GILLEST
JOSEPH SHEVITZ	ROBERT WISCHERMAN
JACOB SHAFFER	JOHN PRIOLETTI
THOMAS JOHNSON	JOSHUA PRICE
ROBERT LAIRD	BETH LYSINGER
ADAM NOSAL	ROBERT GEARHART
KENETH SNYDER	WILLIAM SEILER
LARRY ROBERTS, JR	WALTER CHROBAK
DAVID GUY	GEORGE LIBRANDI
RICHARD MARCHINOSKI, JR	ROBERT SCHORSCH
ALAN T CHAMBERLAIN	SAMUEL FOX
CHARLES PETRO	CARLISLE KAMERER
RUDOLPH FACCHINI	JOHN LECKWART
STANLEY DUZYK	JAMES TAYLOR III
MATT BRUNO	SHANE DOLAND
STANLEY KOSZELA	IVAN CLARK
JOSEPH HURA	MICHELE MALES

ALBERT CASSIDY
RUGGERO PANTANO
DOMINIC SIKORA
SHAWN MACRI
WALTER MUNDZIAK
VINCENT ANGIOLELLI
TERRY CARAVELLA
JOHN MRVAN
BURLIEGH POST, JR
FRANCIS MORRISSEY
LAURA PARDICK
GREGORY ARGIRO
JULIE ANTHONY
THOMAS VAN DRIEL
CLARENCE WEATHERBY
FRANK PETRUCELLI
JACK FRITZ
DARRELL MONTGOMERY
KARL LIECHTY
ALEX LULTSCHIK
PAUL GRAHAM, JR
ANTHONY TOMMASONE
LAWRENCE WEAKLEY
BRADEN BOOHER
FRANK KOMARC
WALTER JOHNSON
MAXWELL ANDORFER
JOSEPH MANCINE
AMANDA KELLEY
STEPHEN SHIPMAN
ROBERT DORAN
HARRY KENEHAN
ROBERT NOLAN
JOSEPH TOMEI

GEORGE BOHIZIC
DENNIS GARGASZ
TED CHROBAK
MERRIL YOUNG
ALBERT MILLIRON
CLYDE WHITTAKER
THOMAS TARNOCI
LARRY RAUSCH
HARRY KELLER, JR
THOMAS LESLIE
SAMUEL JAMES
DAVID STEWART
TODD CRESS
HOWARD CARNES
NEAL FENATI
JOHN HARRISON
GLENN TURNER
DONALD JONES
BRIAN HOLLAND
BERNARD D. SEILER
KEITH CANNON
STEVE SOP
JAMES MCDONALD
ANTHONY PERROTT
CHRISTOPHER MCLEAN
GEORGE PILNER
MELVIN KREBS
AD ROTH
ERICK ECKLUND
WILLIAM CAMPBELL
JL GOOD
ROBERT ENSCOE
JOSHUA GRANT
GEOFFREY SALYERS

CHARLES WARD

MELVIN BOOHER

CURTISS KIRKPATRICK

JOHN POLENICK

RICHARD OWENS

CHRIS SHEVITZ

JOHN STONER

WILLIAM CODY

JONATHAN TENGERES

EDGAR TAYLOR

GEORGE MILES

JAMES STOLE

DIKE BLAIR

JOHN SNIEZEK, SR

RALPH STAPH

LISA BOOK

GEORGE SUMNEY

JOSEPH BURICK

DAVID MCCREARY

THOMAS VILLANI

SUSAN BENDER

WILLIAM A GUIDUCCI

ANTONIO ALBERTINI

SHIRLEY BIGLEY

JOHN MUCHICHO

MARY SCHELL

KRISTOPHER RIGHI

WLADYSLAN POTOCZNY

LEO WOLF

CRAWFORD HARDSOCK

MIKE JACOBS

RALPH HOUK

KENNETH HARRIS

FRANK KOLESAR

WALLY PARDICK

DANIEL STEPHENSON

CHARLES THOMPSON

LEON CHROBAK

YVONNE FYOCK

WALTER STALMA

KENNETH LOCKE

ADAM PARDICK

ANTHONY VITTO

HEATHER SQUARTINO

JOHN ABRAHAM

JOHN BORATKO

KELLY FOX

DAN CULLEN

GEORGE EGGLESTON

DAVID BOSTON

BENJAMIN ANDERSON

EMIL MANCINE

CLAIRE BOOK

CHARLES ABRAMSKI

NICHOLAS DERZYPOLSKI

SAMUEL RHODES

LEONARD WERHNYAK

LLOYD SMITH

GEORGE BOK

CHRIS HALACKNA

DANIEL EMANUELE

JOHN FIRMI

WILLIAM JOHNSTONE

JOSEPH LATESS

DENIS WEIGHT

MARY PERETTI

ARTHUR GALLATIN

GEORGE BLAIR, JR

STANLEY GIERMANSKI

WALTER KOSCIUSKO

FRANK GAYDOSIK

PHILLIP BARTOLONE

JONATHAN REYNOLDS

RICHARD ANTHONY

DAVID ROUDABUSH

KEVIN MCILWAIN

VICTOR LITTERINI

JAMES WOODSIDE

STEVEN RENO

MICHAEL PEPLOWSKI

ANDREW REYNOLDS

JOHN PRESNAR

LEE WHITE

WAYNE MENDT

JOSEPH LAPP

DONALD RODGERS JR

DENNIS GRAY

CHARLES MANCINE

JACK BUCEY

SAMUEL HOUK

JOSEPH PANELLA

WILLIAM WISCHERMAN

CLYDE SNYDER

JOE DIGIAMMARINO

THURMAN POST

KELLY FOX

DAVID WILLIAMS

ROBERT GARDNER

PETE LOVAGLIO

RANDY HINKLE

STEPHEN PETROVITCH

ROBERT WEINGARTNER

EDWARD SHERIDAN

DAVID PASTORE

JAMES PALMER

DONALD RODGERS, III

WARREN COSTAL

JACK RISPOL

NOLA HESSON

ERNIE IAFRAT

SYLVESTER BOCKUM

VINCENT SHOAF

PAUL STRAW

GUISEPPE GUIDUCCI

LEONARD RICH

DEAN FAIR

JOSEPH KOSCIUSKO

NICOLE MAGLIOCCA

NICK CUBELLIS

W. RUSSELL ROHRER

BRIAN DAY

JOHN NELSON

FRANCIS RYZINSKI

VINCENT MAZZOCCO

HOWARD HARTZELL

RUSSELL VOGAN

JACOB SLOSARCSIK

WILLIAM DANGEL

RICHARD GIBSON

CHRISTOPHER WEIGHT

MATTHEW LORELLO

KENNETH GLASGOW

AMON JACOBS

JOHN RICKEL

NORMAN BLACK

BENJAMIN KESSING

FRED KLINK

DAVID BRADLEY

EDDIE BROWN

DAVID WILLIAMS

JOHN SHINGLEDECKER

ROBERT BREST

MICHAEL FLACK

FRED DEPOLIS

ANDY DUGAN

STEVEN LUBINSKI

JOHN SOLONINKA

STEPHEN BURICK

JOSEPH NERO, JR

GEORGE EVANS

EDWARD MARTIN

NICK PAYTO

EVERETT TAYLOR

JEFFREY LUNSFORD

RUSSELL SHAW

EDWARD HATCHNER

GLEN LUTZ

JOSEPH DERICCO

DEMETRI GERMANOS

GEORGE PILNER

DONALD JONES

THOMAS NOLAN

MIKE IAFRAT

JAMES PHILLIPS

BRUCE KINNEY

ROBERT HARRY

JACOB JONES

CHARLES FLEMING

MARK GRUMBINE

DAVID HOGUE

ALEXANDER SNIEZEK

JOHN JOPEK

JOSEPH DERICCO

JOSEPH JAKIELLA

ANDREW CERCELL

MATHEW MCMUNN

WILLIAM RICHARDS

YURKO ROMAN

JOHN MOROCO

PETER VILUTZ

JULIE HUPKO

DAVE MCMILLIN

EMIL GROMMES

NICHOLAS BOWSER

ANDREW NOCERA

JOSEPH DANTICO, JR

THEODORE LELENKO

WILLIAM TANNER, JR

DONALD BOOHER

MICHAEL WOFFORD

DONNA SUE HICKS

WILLIAM PORADA

BONITA BARDASH

PAMILA SMITH

CARLISLE VERNINO

RAY BARTHOLOMEW

NATALIE LOMBARDO

WILLIAM FOREMAN

CLARENCE HANNA

WHITNEY SIMMONS

PAUL SINGER

LUKE DEVITTO

THOMAS GRAHAM

HERMAN SERIGNESE

CHARLES NERO
GARY RALSTON
JEDIDIAH ANDERSON
VICTOR SNIEZEK
KEITH PATTERSON
THOMAS SWEET
MARK NAIL
CARL CARRIER
CHARLES DEMARCO
RONALD ROSS
ALAN C CHAMBERLAIN
FRANK VOGAN
ROBERT MASH
RONALD STILES
JOHN WARSO
BILL CORWIN
ROBERT MILLS
JOHN YAGERSKY
RALPH MURDOCH
JOHN TEPLICA
SCOTT MCDOWELL
SAMUEL LONG
RICHARD GARGASZ
CHARLES MYERS III
JOE TESTA
FRANCIS SOWERSBY
JOHN BERRETT
THOMAS GRIMM
ANTONIA MASTROIANNI
PARK ALCORN
RICHARD SERIGNESE
JACK ALLEN
DOUGLAS MCBRIDE
JAMES FERRARO

MICHAEL ROTH
WALTER MAKAREVICH
RICHARD CARBONE
RANDALL JOHNSON
SAMUEL FLORA
PATRICK SCHOOLEY
FRANK BALLINA
FRANK LECKWART
NORMA JEAN WILKINSON
JOSEPH STAPH
CHARLES SOP
WILLIAM NULPH
DAVID NIMMO
RICHARD BLACK
ANDREW MUCZKO
DWAYNE MAIELLA
JOHN MITCHELL
MARK STAPH
COLLIN REARIGH
JEFFREY WILLIAMS
JOHN BARTKO
WALTER WAID
THOMAS MORRIS
RICHARD POLENICK
JAMES HOAGLAND
WAYNE JORDAN
DONALD JONES
PAUL STALMA
MICHAEL PANDOS
JOSEPH PACE
ARCHIBALD WHITE
ZACHARY KRSTOMICH
WILLIAM LOGAN
STANLEY KOSCIUSKO

WILLIAM NICHOLLS

WILLIAM HACKBARTH

JOSEPH LESNIAK

RONALD COTELESSE

FRANK LONGA

GEORGE BLAIR

ALBERT FORLETTA

ARTHUR BRADLEY

HADDEN BLAIR

STANLEY NYCH

AMERIGO GUIDUCCI

ROBERT JONES

JAMES JOHNSTON

FORTUNATO TROGGIO

MICHAEL ANDREWS

MICHAEL CHOLAK

WARREN ENSCOE

RICHARD ANTHONY

STANLEY GORGACZ

KENNETH CAMERON

JOSEPH OLINGER

WALTER SHAFFER

SALLY PARDICK

WILLIAM BARTHLOW

DENNIS KENNEDY

EDGAR MARTIN, JR

WILLIAM BOGLE

DONALD CRAWFORD

JORDAN WACLAV

PAUL DORAN

AMIEL ATTISANO

JOHN IAFRAT

JOE NYCH

RICHARD BOWSER

MICHAEL RUSSO

SAMUEL RUMMEL

ALBERT NOCERA

DOMINIC NUZZO

NOTES

CHAPTER 1

"I could not help taking: Quoted in Hulbert, 6–7.

That land was calling him: Wolf, unpaginated; Miller, 22.

"John Blair of Fannett Township": Earlier genealogical accounts, including *Meet the Blair Family* by M.A. Miller, suggest that this line of the Blair family descended from a different John Blair, who may have settled first in New England. Using more modern genealogical practices, it appears that John Blair of Fannett Township came directly to Pennsylvania when he emigrated from Ulster in the 1730s.

John's son, Thomas: Most sources say that Thomas Blair was born ca. 1735 in Cumberland County, PA, but according to enlistment records, Thomas may have been born ca. 1733 in County Antrim, Ireland, just before the Blairs immigrated to Pennsylvania.

"with great vigor": Lively descriptions of the missions and expeditions of Captain Thomas Blair and his rangers appear in Jones, *Early History of the Juniata Valley,* 236–246.

"hickory sapling: Ibid., 239.

"notorious: Jones, 244.

"cut both [Hare's] ears: Ibid., 245.

they had been petitioning the county: Miller, 11.

the Juniata ironmaking region: Historian Paul T. Fagley defines the "Juniata Iron District" as "compris[ing] all or parts of the present counties of Perry, Juniata, Mifflin, Centre, Huntingdon, Blair, and Bedford," and notes that Centre County is not within the Juniata River watershed but is considered part of the Juniata Iron District. In: Fagley, "The Romantic Days of Juniata Charcoal Iron," *Pennsylvania History: A Journal of Mid-Atlantic Studies*, 83, no. 2, Special Issue: The Juniata Valley (Spring 2016), 188; 223.

In a letter to a friend dated 1819: Quoted in "First in Our Hearts," *Huntingdon History Research Network.* http://www.huntingdonhistoryresearchnetwork.net/research-topics/first-in-our-hearts/. This excerpt from Whitney's letter may also appear in Albert M. Rung, *Rung's Chronicles of Pennsylvania History* (Huntingdon: Huntingdon County Historical Society, 1977), 275.

"shift the cargo": Zentmyer, 7.

black gnats, rattlesnakes: *The Allegheny Portage Railroad*, Allegheny Portage Railroad National Historic Site, National Park Service: US Department of the Interior, 2009, DVD.

From an early age, John Blair: Miller, 25–29.

newly formed Huntingdon County: Huntingdon County was created from a portion of northern Bedford County on September 20, 1787. A western portion of Huntingdon County would later become Blair County.

Michael Cryder, the owner of a gristmill near Huntingdon: Africa, 31.

In 1807, the state of Pennsylvania appointed: Ibid., 31.

"a real pioneer: Miller, 23.

"had no conception: Ibid.

The proposed route: Africa, 32.

John Blair served: Smith, 20.

he was often spotted along the route: Miller, 33.

the company issued "shinplasters": Ibid., 35.

Records from the Blairsville terminal: Ibid., 38.

a continuous waterway: Jacobs, 3.

"fast new service . . . 23 days . . . five: The Allegheny Portage Railroad, Allegheny Portage Railroad National Historic Site, National Park Service: US Department of the Interior, 2009, DVD.

total of ten inclined planes: The Blair Homestead stands in a small borough called Foot of Ten, which was named for its location at the foot of Incline Plane no. 10 of the Portage Railroad.

"section boats": Section boats eliminated the need to unload and reload the freight; instead, the cargo remained inside the boats and the boats themselves were hauled up and over the mountain in pieces.

1,398 feet up: Baumgardner, 44.

From 1832 to 1835: Visitors Center, Allegheny Portage Railroad National Historic Site, 2017; Jacobs, 14. For more about the Portage Railroad, consider a visit to the Allegheny Portage Railroad Historic Site Visitors Center. The permanent exhibits and introductory film are informative and engaging.

"was drawn by two white horses: quoted in Jacobs, 19.

on November 28, 1932: Miller, 36.

"a slow coach": Jones, 335.

Railroads had several advantages: Paul T. Fagley, "The Romantic Days of Juniata Charcoal Iron," *Pennsylvania History: A Journal of Mid-Atlantic Studies*, 83, no. 2, Special Issue: The Juniata Valley (Spring 2016), 211.

With the completion of the Horseshoe Curve: Ibid., 212-213.

In 1855, the state of Pennsylvania : "Pennsylvania Canal Historical Marker," *ExplorePAHistory.com.* http://explorepahistory.com/hmarker. php?markerId=1-A-1D5.

"*Let us not glory*: Jones, 334 –335.

"*caught the vision*: Miller, 52.

CHAPTER 2

"*There he lived*: Reeve, 15.

He was a captain: Smith, 140.

In 1716, a blacksmith: Bining, 49–50; "Colebrookdale Furnace Historical Marker," *ExplorePAHistory.com*. http://explorepahistory.com/hmarker. php?markerId=1-A-2A3.

by 1775, the American colonies: Gordon, 58.

In 1810, the total national output: "Overview: The Pennsylvania Iron Industry: Furnace and Forge of America," *ExplorePAHistory.com*. http:// explorepahistory.com/story.php?storyId=1-9-17&chapter=0.

At the center of the rural iron plantations: Most of the information about iron plantations is drawn from Mary Wigton Reeve's *Iron Furnace Baronies of Huntingdon County* (1943).

Overseeing it all: Reeve gives a detailed account of life on an iron plantation, including some amusing anecdotes told by people who had grown up on iron plantations in Huntingdon County. Her lengthy discussion of the role of the ironmaster's wife is particularly engaging and offers a different perspective on an industry and social structure dominated by men: "My Lady of the Mansion shared in the joys and sorrows of the workmen's families . . . . Weddings, births, deaths were the responsibility of the family in the Mansion. In poverty there were clothes and supplies sent; in sickness soup and whiskey, quinine and castor oil, and often the children's diseases diagnosed" (11).

"*set well back*: Zentmyer, 22.

Few ironmasters had more success: To date, no book-length biography of Dr. Peter Shoenberger has been written. The most complete portrait of the ironmaster remains Calvin W. Hetrick's 24-page pamphlet, *The Iron King*. Much of the following account of Dr. Shoenberger's career in the iron industry is informed by Hetrick's narrative. All quoted material is from *The Iron King*, unless otherwise specified.

Peter Shoenberger's father, George: Homer T. Rosenberger, "Migrations of the Pennsylvania Germans to Western Pennsylvania, Pt. II," *Western Pennsylvania Historical Magazine*, 54, no. 1 (1971), 58; Paul T. Fagley, "The Romantic Days of Juniata Charcoal Iron," *Pennsylvania History: A Journal of Mid-Atlantic Studies*, 83, no. 2, Special Issue: The Juniata Valley (Spring 2016), 196.

"he was to the iron industry: Quoted in Slusser, 58; Miller, 35.

The mill produced 800 tons: Ingham, *Making Iron and Steel*, 26.

"This is the first great manufactory: Royall, 92–93.

Records from the Blair's Gap terminal: Miller, 35.

CHAPTER 3

"The chief distinction of Pittsburgh: Toker, 1.

the Episcopal Institute: Annie Clark Miller, "Old Houses and Estates in Pittsburgh," *Western Pennsylvania Historical Magazine*, 9, no.3 (July 1926): 135.

He entered Harvard College: All details about Thomas Shoenberger Blair's time at Harvard are drawn from Edward Wheelwright's *The Class of 1844, Harvard College: Fifty Years After Graduation*. Wheelwright, who served as class secretary, notes in the text that he compiled the information about T.S.B. from letters he had received from T.S.B.

"Pig Iron Aristocracy" is a term coined by Quentin R. Skrabec in his book, *The World's Richest Neighborhood: How Pittsburgh's East Enders Forged*

American Industry. (New York: Algora, 2010). For a detailed analysis of the social and economic structures of Pittsburgh's iron and steel industry in the 19th century, see also John N. Ingham's *Making Iron and Steel* and *The Iron Barons.*

the Shoenbergers entertained Dickens: "Section 4 Lot 1: Monuments: Genealogy," *Allegheny Cemetery.* http://www.alleghenycemetery.com/content.php?cat=genealogy&page=monuments&mode=detail&id=15221.

"Pittsburg is like Birmingham: Dickens, 124.

early techniques like blister: Descriptions of blister and crucible steelmaking are drawn from Ingham, *Making Iron and Steel,* 37–39.

the partners were some of the first: Swank, 389–393.

As early as 1847 . . . breakthrough in the steel world: Gordon, 221.

While working on a commission . . . and in large quantities: Misa, 6–9, 15.

He was quick to show off his invention . . . making steel prior to Bessemer: Ibid., 9–14; Gordon, 223–224.

In the ten-year span from 1855 to 1865: Misa, 4.

every few months: "First Steel Rails Historical Marker," *ExplorePAHistory. com.* http://explorepahistory.com/hmarker.php?markerId=1-A-1CA.

"a well-rounded man of culture": Krass, 82.

While in London . . . "without a shilling changing hands": Krass, 87.

"a rail having: Thomas S. Blair. Improvement in Railroad-Rails. US Patent 38,548, May 19, 1963; reissue no. 1,582, December 1, 1863.

"The experiments made: Krass, 88.

In 1867 . . . the nation's circulatory system: "First Steel Rails Historical Marker," *ExplorePAHistory*. http://explorepahistory.com/hmarker. php?markerId=1-A-1CA.
"ordinary iron railroad-rails": Thomas S. Blair. Improved Furnace for Converting Bars into Steel. US Patent 51,289, December 5, 1865.

manufacturing steel from "pig-bloom" and "pig-scrap": Thomas S. Blair. Improvement in the Manufacture of Steel. US Patent 85, 053, December 22, 1868.

the use of an apparatus: Thomas S. Blair. Improved Apparatus for the Manufacture of Pig-Blooms. US Patent 91,901, June 29, 1869.

two British patents: Thomas S. Blair. Improvements in converting cast iron into wrought iron, and in uniting oxides and fluxes with molten cast iron. GB Patent 2968, September 28, 1868; Thomas S. Blair. Improvements in the manufacture of steel. GB Patent 3631, November 28, 1868. Both patent applications are listed in Bennet Woodcroft, *Chronological Index of Patentees and Applicants for Patents of Invention For the Year 1868*. London: Order of the Commissioners of Patents, 1869.

"embod[ied] the latest and most advanced ideas": Thomas S. Blair, "The 'Direct Process' of Iron Manufacture," in *Transactions of the American Institute of Mining Engineers Vol. 2* (Easton, PA.: American Institute of Mining Engineers, 1875): 179.

In May 1872, Blair was granted a patent . . . and was issued two additional patents: Thomas S. Blair. Improvement in the Manufacture of Wrought-Iron and Steel From Iron Sponge. US Patent 126,923, May 21, 1872; Thomas S. Blair. Improvement in Iron Sponge. US Patent 126,924, May 21, 1872; Thomas S. Blair. Improvement in Processes and Apparatus for Reducing the Ores of Iron. US Patent 126,922, May 21, 1872.

"The iron sponge which I manufacture: Thomas S. Blair. Improvement in Iron Sponge. US Patent 126,924, May 21, 1872.

The open-hearth process took much longer: Joseph S. Spoerl, "A Brief History of Iron and Steel Production" (unpublished manuscript, 2004), PDF.

CHAPTER 4

"A lifetime seems: Miller, 53.

spent two decades trying to make the process work: Ingham, *Making Iron and Steel*, 40–41.

He hired a scholarly young engineer: John Stubbles, "Who Was Henry Howe?" *Metallurgical and Materials Transactions B*, 29B (February 1998): 9.

Blair wanted to use a Siemens: Thomas S. Blair, "The 'Direct Process' of Iron Manufacture," in *Transactions of the American Institute of Mining Engineers Vol. 2* (Easton, PA.: American Institute of Mining Engineers, 1875), 191.

"There has been a link missing: Ibid., 181.

"associate and colaborer: Ibid., 196.

"I refer to the humanitarian view: Ibid., 195–196.

"Ammonia (spirits of hartshorn): Ibid., 197.

"As a humanitarian, I am delighted . . . overgrown, *not* overthrown.*"*: Ibid., 198.

a US patent: Thomas S. Blair. Improvement in the Manufacture of Steel by the Open-Hearth Process. US Patent 155, 136, filed June 24, 1874, and issued September 22, 1874.

"Our books, showing the exact amount: Morrison Foster, letter to the editor, *Scientific American*, June 19, 1875.

"the direct process : Isaac Lowthian Bell. "Notes of a Visit to the Coal- and Iron-Mines and Ironworks in the United States," *The Journal of the Iron and Steel Institute* (1875): 127–129.

"This remarkable and interesting fact: Morrison Foster, letter to the editor, *Scientific American*, June 19, 1875.

"still fresh in the minds: Mr. I. Lowthian Bell and the Blair Direct Process (Pittsburgh: James McMillan, 1875): 9.

Holley defended Blair's claims: Ibid., 14.

"glad to be able to confirm Mr. Holley's statements: Ibid., 14.

Howe devoted several pages to Blair's Direct Process: Howe, 281.

for a career in metallurgy outside steel mills: John Stubbles, "Who Was Henry Howe?" *Metallurgical and Materials Transactions B*, 29B (February 1998): 9.

"I have attributed the failure: Howe, 281.

"An invention must be nursed: Quoted in Misa, 11.

"a relatively stable: Ingham, *Iron Barons*, xiii.

In late summer 1875, the Edgar Thomson Works: Misa, 22; Krass 117–119, 128.

"large, integrated: Ingham, *Iron Barons*, xiii

"a majority of: Ingham, *Making Iron and Steel*, 84.

sued for a refund of the capital stock: Morgan's case against Thomas S. Blair and his lawyer, Thomas Struthers, was ultimately heard by the United States Supreme Court: Morgan v. Struthers, 131 US 234 (1889).

a pair of blast furnaces: Kobus, 136.

As competitors Carnegie Steel: Ingham, *Making Iron and Steel*, 87–88.

"Personally, Mr. Blair was a delightful companion: "Thomas S. Blair's Career Is Ended," *Pittsburgh Daily Post*, Oct. 23, 1898.

"the Town of Pittsburgh: Kussart, 74.

endowed St. Margaret Memorial Hospital: "Our History," UPMC St. Margaret: *UPMC*. http://www.upmc.com/locations/hospitals/st-margaret/about/Pages/history.aspx.

"seated, facing right: Beal, 18, 358.

"little treatise: Blair, *Human Progress*, i.

"an enlightened self-interest: Ibid., 533.

"nothing more than a connected series of suggestions: Ibid., i.

"[It] throws an absolutely new light: Gunton, 268.

CHAPTER 5

We just developed an idea: Ford, 75.

up to 140,000 bricks per day: "Brick by the Million," *The Chicago Tribune*, October 18, 1872.

"the busiest stop: "Tyrone, PA (TYR)," *The Great American Stations Project*. http://www.greatamericanstations.com/stations/tyrone-pa-tyr/. Ralph T. Wolfgang's *A Short History of Tyrone Borough*, published by the Tyrone Area Historical Society, gives a clear, lovingly crafted account of Tyrone's history from 1850-1950. W.H. Wilson's *Tyrone of Today*, published in 1897, is a valuable resource as well.

one of the most productive: "Sandy Ridge History," *Mountain Top Fire Company*. http://mountaintopfireco13.org/custom.html?id=2945.

one of the last places: "Two Rich Hauls," *Pittsburgh Commercial Gazette*, January 22, 1898.

population of New Castle in 1890 . . . had reached 38,280 people: "Our History," *New Castle, Pennsylvania*. http://www.newcastlepa.org/History/history.html.

influx of immigrants . . . seeking jobs in the mills: Anthony B. Toth, "The Syrian Community in New Castle and Its Unique Alawi Component," *The Western Pennsylvania Historical Magazine* 69, no. 3 (July 1986): 222-224.

Noah W. Elliott and George Elliott: Most of the information about the Elliott family of cold-rolled steelmakers and the iterations of their steel companies was drawn from Aaron L. Hazen, *20th Century History of New Castle and Lawrence County Pennsylvania and Representative Citizens* (Chicago: Richmond-Arnold, 1908); "Elliott-Blair Steel Co. Announces Important Change," *New Castle Herald*, April 7, 1923; bulletins published in *The Iron Age,* April 7, 1898 and January 18, 1912; and interviews with Thomas C. Elliott II and Thomas C. Elliott III in April 2014.

first president of the New Castle Golf Club . . . designed by A. W. Tillinghast: Jack Winter, "The Early Days," History: *New Castle Country Club*. https://newcastlecc.org/index.cfm?ID=113.

"There is every indication: "New Industry to be Started Soon," *New Castle News,* November 27, 1923.

"I will build a motor car for the great multitude: This famous quotation appears in Ford's book, *My Life and Work,* published in 1923, but according to historian Douglas Brinkley, the June 1913 issue of the *Ford Times* claims that Ford made the statement around 1903 when the Ford Motor Company was founded.

the base price of the Model T: Brinkley, 111, 186.

"The appeal of Ford's 'car: Ibid., 118.

sold more than 15 million: Ibid., xxii.

In 1914 alone: Ibid., xvi.

two-thirds of all vehicles: Ibid., 129.

"The Blair Strip Steel company is directly: "East Side Site is Taken by Blair Strip Steel Co. to Build a New Plant," *New Castle News*, January 28, 1924.

40 percent of the world's iron and steel: "About AISI," History of The AISI: *American Iron and Steel Institute*. http://www.steel.org/about-aisi/history.aspx.

"In his departure hence: "In Memoriam: George Blair," a resolution offered by the board of directors of the First National Bank of Lawrence County, May 21, 1928.

CHAPTER 6

"Sooner or later: Quoted in Galbraith, 84.

"We are unable to obtain: "Former N.C. Man Talks of Life in Old England," *New Castle Herald*, February 13, 1918.

"wartime 'Pittsburgh Colony: Ibid.

"on grounds of indignities: "Lady Thornton Wins Philadelphia Divorce," *The New York Times*, July 28, 1926.

"an extended trip East: "Solemnize Wedding of Dover Society Girl," *The Daily Times*, June 9, 1913.

"best ringer score: "Golf Champion is Crowned at Trophy Dinner," *New Castle News*, October 17, 1921.

"necessary to give: "Let Contract for City Hall Wiring," *New Castle News*, August 29, 1924.

"dashing . . . first pitch: "Hoover Hurls First Ball In Series Of 1930," *New Castle News*, October 1, 1930.

At 6:20: Most of the account of the fire at Blair Strip Steel and its aftermath was taken from the story, "Old Main Plant of Blair Steel Company Burns," which ran in the evening edition of the *New Castle News*, October 1, 1930.

"While crowds milled: Ibid.

"15,000 square feet . . . the material loss: "Will Rebuild Blair Plant," *New Castle News*, October 2, 1930.

"Please accept the thanks: "Firemen Receive Check for $100," *New Castle News*, October 7, 1930.

George Blair stated publicly: "Will Rebuild Blair Plant," *New Castle News*, October 2, 1930.

While the company secured: "Brick Work Started on New Blair Strip Steel Mill Building," *New Castle News*, December 4, 1930.

the water pressure: "City Wants to Know Pressure," *New Castle News*, January 19, 1931.

"The steel industry will lead: "Chas. M. Schwab Says Steel Will Lead March to Prosperity," *New Castle News*, October 24, 1930.

In 1929, steelmakers operated . . . 19.9 percent of plant capacity: Rogers, 68–69.

Lewis filed a patent: Lester L. Lewis. Annealing Apparatus. US Patent 1,777,978, filed December 2, 1929, and issued October 7, 1930.

He was granted two: Lester L. Lewis. Annealing Art. US Patent 1,898,674, filed September 3, 1930, and issued February 21, 1933; Lester L. Lewis. Art of Annealing Metal Work. US Patent 1,870,126, filed February 17, 1930, and issued August 2, 1932.

He developed a device: "Local Inventor Perfects Device for Blind Flying," *New Castle News*, August 15, 1931.

Blair Strip Steel conformed: "Wage Increase at Blair Strip Steel," *New Castle News,* July 19, 1933.

"We expect to have: "Increase Production at Blair Strip Steel," *New Castle News*, February 10, 1934.

ten-percent wage increase: "Expect Many to Benefit From Wage Increase," *New Castle News*, March 29, 1934.

Because NIRA authorized: Irving Bernstein, "Chapter 5: Americans in Depression and War," *United States Department of Labor*. https://www.dol.gov/general/aboutdol/history/chapter5.

From 1930–32, auto production . . . Roaring Twenties: Rogers, 72.

The steel industry: Rogers, 68.

George Blair pledged $20,000. . . individual donor: "Hospital Fund is Over $200,000 With Noon Reports Today," *New Castle News*, December 16, 1947.

CHAPTER 7

Details and anecdotes about the lives of Tom Blair, Dike Blair, and Phyllis Blair are drawn from interviews with Reba Blair, Kate Blair, Susan Johnson, Phyllis Blair, and Hadden Blair conducted 2014–2017.

Dike and Tom Blair grew up: These details from Tom Blair's and Dike Blair's childhood years in New Castle are drawn from the unpublished autobiographical writings of Dike Blair, courtesy of the Blair family.

tens of thousands of people: Joseph, 21.

the humorous narrative advertisements: Dike Blair published his ads in a collection called *Books and Bedlam: Zany Fictional Adventures of a Bookseller in a Vermont College Town* (Middlebury: Vermont Books): 1962. It's a whimsical read for anyone who loves the places that are now called "small, independent bookstores" and is amused by the quirks of a college town.

CHAPTER 8

Details and anecdotes about the history and operations of Blair Strip Steel are drawn from interviews with Blair retirees, employees, and board members conducted 2014–2019.

led the world in steel production: Some sources say the US was producing as much as 72 percent of the world's steel. This number is plausible because the US was the only major producer whose economy, infrastructure, and workforce were not devastated by the war.

"Push-n-Puller": Though "Push-n-Puller" may not be the exact or official title of the position, it was probably a job that was as physically demanding as it sounds. When Tucker Nolan started at Blair in the late 1920s, annealing was done in an annealing room, which was lined with firebricks and heated with coal to bring the steel up to temperatures of 1100-1200°F. The coils of steel were loaded onto a heavy plate that was slid into the annealing room atop cannon balls set into a shallow groove in the floor. It took several men (usually 8 or more—a whole "furnace gang") using metal poles to push the plate of coils into the room. Four or five days later, after the coils had been carefully heated, held at temperature, then slowly cooled down, it was time to retrieve them. The doors to the annealing room would be opened, and the plate would be hooked with long leather harnesses. The same men who pushed the plate of coils into the room would shoulder the harnesses and pull the plate back out. This hard, hot work was typically assigned to the younger, stronger men.

CHAPTER 9

Details and anecdotes in this chapter are drawn from interviews conducted with Bruce Kinney and Hadden Blair 2013–2019.

CHAPTER 10

Details about BelleFlex Technologies and PulFlex Technologies are drawn from interviews conducted with Bruce Kinney 2018–2019.

CHAPTER 11

Details and anecdotes in this chapter are drawn from interviews with Blair retirees, employees, and board members 2013–2019.

"Teams desiring games: "Blair Steel Team is Now in Field," *New Castle News*, June 5, 1929.

"allowed but four hits: "Blair Steel Team Tops Missions 7-2," *New Castle News*, June 26, 1929.

"Attn: Scott A. McDowell and Bruce Kinney: Adapted faithfully from a letter written by Mrs. Edna Hritz, undated.

"Dear Friends at Blair Strip Steel: Quoted from a letter written by Mr. James D. Phillips, dated June 2014.

EPILOGUE

88 million tonnes . . . 996 million tonnes: "Steelmaking Capacity," "World Crude Steel Production - Summary," World Steel Association. https://www.worldsteel.org/media-centre/press-releases/2020/Global-crude-steel-output-increases-by-3.4--in-2019.html. Accessed 14 July 2020.

SELECTED BIBLIOGRAPHY

The following list includes many of the sources that are referenced in the notes of this book, as well as other texts that are not directly referenced but nonetheless provided valuable historical context and color. Many of the bibliographies I encountered during the research process were tremendously helpful; may this bibliography aid other researchers and authors along the way.

Africa, J. Simpson. *History of Huntingdon and Blair Counties, Pennsylvania.* Philadelphia: Louis H. Everts, 1883.

Baumgardner, Mahlon J. and Floyd G. Hoenstine. *The Allegheny Old Portage Railroad 1834–1854.* 1952.

Beal, Rebecca J. *Jacob Eichholtz 1776–1842, Portrait Painter of Pennsylvania.* Philadelphia: The Historical Society of Pennsylvania, 1969.

Bining, Arthur C. *Pennsylvania Iron Manufacture in the Eighteenth Century.* Harrisburg, PA: The Pennsylvania Historical Commission, 1938.

Blair, Thomas S. *Human Progress: What Can Man Do to Further It?* New York: William R. Jenkins, 1896.

Blair, Thomas S. "The 'Direct Process' of Iron Manufacture." In *Transactions of the American Institute of Mining Engineers Vol. 2,* 175–199. Easton, PA.: American Institute of Mining Engineers, 1875.

Brinkley, Douglas. *Wheels for the World: Henry Ford, His Company, and a Century of Progress.* New York: Viking, 2003.

Churella, Albert J. *The Pennsylvania Railroad, Volume 1: Building an Empire, 1846–1917.* Philadelphia: UPenn Press, 2012.

Dickens, Charles. *American Notes, Pictures of Italy, and A Child's History of England.* London: Chapman and Hall, 1891.

Donehoo, George P. *Pennsylvania: A History*. New York: Lewis Historical Publishing, 1926.

Ford, Henry with Samuel Crowther. *My Life and Work*. New York: Doubleday, 1923.

Galbraith, John Kenneth. *The Great Crash: 1929*. Houghton Mifflin Harcourt: 1997.

Gordon, Robert B. *American Iron 1607-1900*. Baltimore: The Johns Hopkins University Press, 1996.

Gunton, George, ed. *Gunton's Magazine Vol. XII*. New York: Political Science Pub. Co., 1897.

Hazen, Aaron L. *20th Century History of New Castle and Lawrence County Pennsylvania and Representative Citizens*. Chicago: Richmond-Arnold, 1908.

Hetrick, Calvin T. *The Iron King*. Martinsburg, PA.: Morrisons Cove Herald, 1961.

Hoenstine, Floyd G., George A. Wolf, and Blair County Historical Society. *Blair County's First Hundred Years, 1846–1946*. Hollidaysburg, PA.: Blair County Historical Society, 1945.

Howe, Henry Marion. *The Metallurgy of Steel, Vol. 1*. New York: Scientific Pub. Co., 1892.

Hulbert, Archer B. *The Paths of Inland Commerce: A Chronicle of Trail, Road, and Waterway*. New Haven: Yale UP, 1920.

Ingham, John N. *The Iron Barons: A Social Analysis of an American Urban Elite, 1874-1965*. Westport, CT.: Greenwood Press, 1978.

Ingham, John N. *Making Iron and Steel: Independent Mills in Pittsburgh, 1820-1920*. Columbus: Ohio State University Press, 1991.

Jacobs, Harry A. *The Juniata Canal and Old Portage Railroad*. Hollidaysburg, PA: Blair County Historical Society, 1941.

Jones, U.J., *Early History of the Juniata Valley* with notes and extensions by Floyd G. Hoenstine. Harrisburg, PA: The Telegraph Press, 1940.

Joseph, Timothy. *Historic Photographs of The Manhattan Project*. Nashville: Turner Publishing Co., 2009.

Kobus, Kenneth J. *City Of Steel: How Pittsburgh Became the World's Steelmaking Capital During the Carnegie Era*. Lanham, MD.: Rowman and Littlefield, 2015.

Krass, Peter. *Carnegie*. New York: Wiley & Sons, 2003.

Kussart, S. *The Early History of the Fifteenth Ward of the City Of Pittsburgh*. Bellevue, PA: Suburban printing Company, 1925. Accessed at http://files.usgwarchives.net/pa/allegheny/history/local/kussart61-90.txt.

Meyer, Mark and Meredith Meyer Grelli. *The Whiskey Rebellion and the Rebirth of Rye: A Pittsburgh Story*. Cleveland: Belt Publishing, 2017.

Miller, M.A. *Meet the Blair Family*. Altoona, PA.: The Mirror Press, 1946.

Misa, Thomas J. *A Nation of Steel: The Making of Modern America 1865–1925*. Baltimore: Johns Hopkins UP, 1995.

Reeve, Mary Wigton. *Iron Furnace Baronies of Huntingdon County*. Clearfield, PA: 1943.

Rogers, Robert P. *An Economic History of the American Steel Industry*. London: Routledge, 2009.

Royall, Anne Newport. *Mrs. Royall's Pennsylvania, or Travels Continued in the United States, Vol. 1 and 2*. Washington, DC: 1829.

Schumacher, E.F. *Small is Beautiful: Economics as if People Mattered*. Point Roberts, WA.: Hartley & Marks, 1999.

Skrabec, Quentin R. *The World's Richest Neighborhood: How Pittsburgh's East Enders Forged American Industry*. New York: Algora, 2010.

Slowik, Teresa J. *America's Art, Smithsonian American Art Museum.* Washington, DC : Smithsonian American Art Museum, 2006.

Slusser, Dale Wayne. *The Ravenscroft School in Asheville: A History of the Institution and Its People and Buildings.* Jefferson, NC: McFarland & Co, 2014.

Smith, Larry D. *150ᵗʰ Anniversary of Blair County, Pennsylvania.* Apollo, PA: Closson Press, 1997.

Smith, Robert Walter. *History of Armstrong County, Pennsylvania.* Chicago: Waterman, Watkins, & Co., 1883.

Swank, James Moore. *History of the Manufacture of Iron in All Ages and Particularly in the United States from Colonial Times to 1891.* Cambridge: Cambridge UP, 2011.

Wheelwright, Edward. *The Class of 1844, Harvard College: Fifty Years After Graduation.* Cambridge: John Wilson and Son, 1896.

Thurston, George Henry. *Allegheny County's Hundred Years.* Pittsburgh: A.A. Anderson and Son, 1888.

Toker, Franklin. *Pittsburgh: An Urban Portrait.* University Park, PA.: Penn State UP, 1986.

Wiley, Samuel T. *Biographical and Portrait Cyclopedia of Blair Co., PA.* Philadelphia, 1892.

Wolf, George A., ed. *Frankstown Township Huntingdon County, Pennsylvania in 1790.* Altoona, PA: Blair County Historical Society, 1964.

Wolfgang, Ralph T. *A Short History of Tyrone Borough.* Tyrone, PA.: Tyrone Historical Society, 1950.

Zentmyer, R.A. *Early Iron Works of Central Pennsylvania.* Altoona, PA: The Altoona Tribune, 1916.

ACKNOWLEDGMENTS

When Bruce Kinney hired me to research and write the history of the Blair Strip Steel Company, neither he nor I knew exactly what this project would entail. We knew the objective—to trace the path from the early days of the Blairs' involvement in iron and steel, to the company's founding, to its hundredth birthday—and we knew the purpose—to honor the extraordinary people who created and sustained an extraordinary company—but we could not have guessed the scope and depth the project would take on. Thank you for your trust, BK; for knowing I would approach the task with respect and care; for helping me find and follow intriguing sidebars in the historical record; for the chance to give voice to a story that had not yet been told. There is always more, but for now, there is this: the first comprehensive history of Blair Strip Steel.

This book would not have been possible without the generous cooperation of the Blair family. Hadden Blair served not only as a connector and a source of Blair family history, he also provided insights into Blair Strip Steel that no one else could have offered. Hadden, your editorial input about contemporary Blair made the book far better and more historically significant than it would have been otherwise. Thank you.

I am deeply grateful to the late Phyllis Blair for welcoming me into her life for a weekend in July 2014. She shared stories from her life with Tom Blair and their remarkable family and gave me a glimpse into her own history as an individual and an artist. Our time together, albeit brief, left a lasting impression on the way I perceive my roles as wife, mother, and artist.

I offer sincere gratitude to Kate Blair, Susan Johnson, and the late Reba Blair for the time they spent with me in 2014 and all the stories and resources they have shared with me. Their genealogical prowess and family archives both launched the research for this book and deepened it. I could not have included so many historical details if they had not been such careful and generous custodians of those artifacts, most especially Dike Blair's autobiographical writings. I am also grateful to Joan Dix Blair and Dike Blair for their permission to use several images that appear in this book and for their assistance with those images.

There would be no book in the material sense without the professionals at Parafine Press. Thank you to Anne Trubek for creating a home for projects like this and for answering my myriad questions; to Dan Crissman for his skillful editing and patient management of a project with multiple stakeholders; and Meredith Pangrace for designing not merely a book but an artifact.

In a company like Blair (or perhaps in any company), there is only so much that paper records can tell us. Without the conversations I had with Blair board members, employees, and retirees, the story would have lacked the personality and affection that are utterly elemental to the culture of the company.

Thank you, board members George Weingartner and Brenda McBride, for our rich conversations and your trust in me and the process. A special thank you to Glenn Turner for countless conversations and his memory for details. Glenn, I can't thank you enough for putting up with my technical questions and obsessive fact checking. Board member and company president Scott McDowell has trusted the purpose of this project and has supported our efforts all along the way. Thank you, Scott, for letting BK and me run with this and for your sharp eye and smart input.

I was extremely fortunate to have extensive conversations with Beth Lysinger, John Avau, Karen Ippolito, Dick Black, Ken Harris, and the late Jack Allen. Each of you made the book better than it would have been without your stories and insights. Thank you, Dr. Gordon Wilber, for sharing your expertise and knowledge at crucial points in the project. Thanks also for coming up with a very snappy title.

Thank you to all the Blair employees and retirees who were willing to talk about their experiences, including Norman Black, Rich Carbone, Dick Enscoe, Warren Enscoe, David Guy, Steve Keller, George Pilner, Clyde Rodgers, Dominic Sikora, Jack Stoner, and Sam Tieche.

I am grateful to all the members of the Blair community who contributed photos, newspaper clippings, letters, and other artifacts, whether we were able to include them in the book or not. Sincere thanks to Clyde Rodgers for the "Horsing Around" clipping; James D. Phillips and Edna Hritz for their thoughtful letters; Glenn Turner for a great many photos; and Darrell Montgomery for the photo from Glen Lutz's retirement party. Thank you also to Bill Kingzett for capturing the joy of the Blair 90th birthday celebration and to Maria McKee and Mary Flagg Lewis of the Lawrence County YMCA for their assistance and permission to use a reproduction of Phyllis E. Blair's painting, *Ballet*.

I am grateful for the time I was able to spend with the late Thomas C. Elliott II and Thomas C. Elliott III in 2014. Thank you for your reflections on Elliott Bros. Steel Co. and the steel industry in New Castle.

I could not have imagined how significantly genealogical research would shape the narrative of the early days of the Blairs of Blair's Gap. Charlotte Blair Stewart's meticulous research and faithful interpretation of the genealogical record was crucial to the story. I am so grateful for her work on our behalf. Margaret Skrivseth, Don Feathers, fellow researcher Larry Phillips, and the volunteers of the Blair County Genealogical Society were also indispensable as we attempted to connect the dots.

My grandmother, Eloise Schaefer Tressel, first inspired my respect for those who devote their time and energy to their local historical societies. Doing research for this book has increased my respect tenfold. Thank you to Susan Linville of the Lawrence County Historical Society; Mary Alice Weckerly, Larry Clever, and Ed Clarke of the Armstrong County Historical Society; and Cathy Horner of the Centre County Historical Society.

Librarians are pretty much superheroes, and I was fortunate to work with several generous ones, including Emilee Gustkey of the New Castle Public Library; Jackie Rhule of the Martinsburg Community Library; Caralee Sommerer of the Carnegie Library of Pittsburgh; and Mary Margaret Carr, Fine Arts Specialist with the General Services Administration. No one was more helpful at pivotal moments than my hometown librarians Rachel Kuhn and Kim Hunter of the Jasper County Public Library in Rensselaer. They found a way to access an article by Thomas Shoenberger Blair that I thought I would never be able to get my hands on and filled innumerable book requests via Indiana's SRCS. When the table in the genealogy alcove became my second home, they always asked how the work was going and indulged my need for a little human interaction.

I experienced many lucky breaks during the research process, most notably on a research trip to central Pennsylvania. I am forever grateful to Nancy Smith of the Tyrone Area Historical Society for putting me in touch with Ned Newlin; to Ned, Relda, and Matthew Newlin for sharing Huntingdon Furnace with my photographer and me; and to Brian McCoy for letting us experience the Blair Homestead up close.

"My" photographer is the travel photographer Whitney Tressel, who contributed many of the original images in this book. She is, bar none, the best research travel partner, collaborator, and early reader a writer could ask for and the greatest, most inspiring sister.

I became a mother while working on this project, and I was able to see the book through to completion thanks to all the help I received, including from the loving child care providers and early educators in my life. Their work is undervalued yet utterly priceless. Thank you to Leslie Smith; the teachers and staff at Families of JCYC, including Masako Chapman,

Madison Klingler, Theresa Cole, and Leann Corbin; Regan Rodibaugh; Beth Hopkins; Meredith Lucero; Carla Luzadder; Natalie Zacher; and Stephanie Brooks.

I could not ask for better friends and colleagues, near and far. My heartfelt thanks to each of you for the particular ways you have encouraged me during this project: Sarah and Jake Zager, Brenda and Tony Butler (for the signage), Michelle Potter, Renee Overbeck, Shannon Kozyra, Addie Scheurich, Kayla Neibert, the R&R Book Group, Abbie Parmele, Judy Beehler, Holly Hopkins, Marcia Smith-Wood, Meghan and Lisa Maloney-Vinz, Josiah and Jamie Titus, Courtney Johnson, Cherish Orozco, Christine Oryhan, Colleen Ruggieri, Charlie M. Hartman, Tania Lemos, Todd C. Harris, Kate Eidam, Kimberly Laird, Sarah Turner Litz, Libby Sutherland, Laura Mogulich, Shawn Tiberio, Diana Tucker, Cassandra Snyder, Mildred Schaefer Levine, and Joann Schaefer Brown.

Thank you to my fellow members of the Prairie Writers Guild, especially Connie Kingman and John Groppe; to Judy Kanne, Janett Kingman, and Jane Lord of the Jasper County Historical Society and Wendy Schwab of BRICKS for giving me exactly the right places to work right when I needed them; to Christy Fleming and Peggy Smith for coffee, "casseroles," and all those times you lent me a kind ear and checked on me upstairs; to Alida Winternheimer, Pete Beatty, Marian Calabro, and Jacqueline Marino for wise counsel; to Pam Hueser for always believing in the bigger picture; and to Brienne Hooker for helping me remember who I was writing for.

I am perpetually grateful for the love and support of my parents, Jim and Ellen Tressel and Carol and Kurt Zabel, and my brother, Zak Tressel. Thank you for cheering me on, no matter what.

Dan and Gayle Alson are so much more than in-laws. They are generous parents, loving grandparents, loyal business partners, devoted readers, seasoned cemetery finders, and our friendliest neighbors on the compound. Your help, support, and belief in my jamming abilities have kept me going. Thank you for everything you have done for me and for us.

I thought this book would be my first baby, and I am happy to be wrong. JJ and RM, thank you for being your wondrous selves and for papering my office with your Post-it Note artwork when I became too focused.

Somehow it always comes back to Adam. (Always has.) Adam, you believed so faithfully in me and the work that matters to me that you agreed to go to the Blair 90th birthday celebration the day after our wedding. For that day and every day since, thank you.

ABOUT THE AUTHOR

photo: Brincefield Studios

Carlee Tressel Alson is an independent writer and editor who has helped numerous corporations, small businesses, non-profits, entrepreneurs, and fellow writers tell their stories. Her own creative work has appeared in a variety of publications, including *Car Bombs to Cookie Tables: The Youngstown Anthology, Casing Sport Communication, The Under Review,* and *Belt Magazine.* She is a graduate of the University of Chicago and holds an MFA from Hamline University. Raised in Youngstown, Ohio, Carlee now lives and farms with her family in northwest Indiana.